THE THIRD DIMENSION IN CHEMISTRY

THE
THIRD DIMENSION IN CHEMISTRY

BY

A. F. WELLS

OXFORD
AT THE CLARENDON PRESS

Oxford University Press, Amen House, London E.C.4
GLASGOW NEW YORK TORONTO MELBOURNE WELLINGTON
BOMBAY CALCUTTA MADRAS KARACHI LAHORE DACCA
CAPE TOWN SALISBURY NAIROBI IBADAN ACCRA
KUALA LUMPUR HONG KONG

FIRST PUBLISHED 1956
REPRINTED LITHOGRAPHICALLY IN GREAT BRITAIN
AT THE UNIVERSITY PRESS, OXFORD
BY VIVIAN RIDLER, PRINTER TO THE UNIVERSITY
FROM CORRECTED SHEETS OF THE FIRST EDITION
1962

PREFACE

MOST people will probably agree that some knowledge of chemistry should form part of a general education. A real understanding of structural chemistry calls for some appreciation of the third dimension, and for some time I have had the idea that this aspect of the subject could profitably be linked up with certain parts of geometry which sometimes receive less attention than they merit. In this little book I have attempted to express that idea. Those whose task it is to teach chemistry will be more competent to assess the value of this approach and to adapt and develop it to suit particular needs.

The teaching of chemistry, and in particular that of inorganic chemistry, has been profoundly influenced in one respect by the historical development of the subject. For a long time chemistry was essentially the study of the behaviour of finite groups of atoms, the molecules and complex ions which exist in solution or in the vapour state. The study of gases and of reactions between gases played a very important part in establishing the laws of chemical combination and in indicating the correct relation between atoms and molecules, so making possible the determination of atomic weights. The development of the very extensive chemistry of carbon compounds focused attention on the molecule as the ultimate unit of a compound corresponding to the atom in the case of an element.

It is true that certain reactions involving solids (for example, the oxidation of a metal or the formation of a number of oxides) were also of great importance in the early studies and, of course, many elements and compounds are obtained as solids at ordinary temperatures. Their chemistry is, however, studied by breaking them down, usually by dissolution, and observing the behaviour of the units present in the solution. It is, perhaps, not surprising that chemists came to regard solid inorganic, as well as organic, compounds as built of discrete molecules.

The composition of a solid is found by chemical analysis, which tells us the relative numbers of the atoms of various kinds in the solid; it gives no information about the arrangement of the atoms. In the case of an organic compound the crystal consists of the same molecules as those which can be studied in solution or in the vapour. This is also true of some solid inorganic compounds, notably the compounds of the less metallic elements one with another, but in crystals of many compounds of the more metallic elements there is no molecule corresponding to the empirical formula or a small multiple of it. When a crystal of such a compound is dissolved or vaporized there is inevitably a considerable rearrangement of the atoms, so that there is generally no simple relation between the structure of the substance in the solid state and in solution. In the crystal, but not in solution, there can exist arrangements of atoms which extend indefinitely in one, two, or three dimensions.

Although these possibilities were appreciated at a much earlier date by some crystallographers and, indeed, the structures of some crystals were predicted more than seventy years ago, they could not be verified until it became possible to study the atomic structures of crystals. Since von Laue's demonstration of the diffraction of X-rays by crystals in 1912 a great deal has been learnt about the atomic structures of crystalline materials of many kinds, but we cannot do justice to this great extension of structural chemistry by adding a few diagrams of crystal structures to a conventional text.

The aim of this book is to help the student of chemistry to appreciate the nature of this development so that he will come to regard the three-dimensional arrangements of atoms in crystals as an integral part of structural chemistry, and their formation as the logical result of the same processes that are responsible for the formation of smaller groups of atoms. It may seem odd that no mention is made of structural chemistry in the first two-thirds of the book. I am not, however, concerned here with the details of this subject, and I have not attempted a systematic treatment; the problem is one of mental outlook, and this is why I have started with polygons and polyhedra. These are highly interesting objects in themselves, but what is more important is the fact that they have a great deal to do with structural chemistry.

The nature of the subject-matter makes it difficult to illustrate adequately a book of this kind even with the aid of stereoscopic photographs. The value of models can hardly be overemphasized, and fortunately it is quite easy to build satisfactory models like those illustrated at a very small cost. A great deal can be done with materials as simple as cork or table-tennis balls, bicycle spokes, and sheets of celluloid or other similar material.

I wish to acknowledge with gratitude permission to reproduce the following illustrations: Fig. 5 (*a*), from the Trustees of the British Museum; Fig. 8, from the *Transactions of the American Institute of Mining and Metallurgical Engineers* (and Professor C. S. Smith and Dr. W. M. Williams); Figs. 17 and 19, from *Acta Crystallographica;* Fig. 26, from *Growth and Form* by D'Arcy W. Thompson (Cambridge University Press); Fig. 37, from *The Structure and Properties of Solid Surfaces* edited by R. Gomer and C. S. Smith (University of Chicago Press); Fig. 63, from *Mineralogy* by H. A. Miers (Macmillan & Co. Ltd.); Fig. 71, from the *Journal of the Textile Institute* (and Dr. H. J. Woods); Fig. 74, from *The Crystalline State* (Volume 1) by W. L. Bragg (G. Bell and Sons, Ltd.); Figs. 98 and 101, from Quarterly Reviews (The Chemical Society, London). Figs. 43, 78, 80, 81, 84, 85, 86, 90, 93, and 94 are reproduced from the author's *Structural Inorganic Chemistry* (Clarendon Press).

For their kindness in providing original photographs I wish to thank Professor W. T. Astbury (Fig. 9 (*a*)), Dr. G. H. Francis (Fig. 7 (*a*)), Dr. J. L. Moilliet (Fig. 9 (*b*)), Mr. H. M. Powell (Fig. 99), and my colleague Mr. E. Young and his staff for preparing the elegant stereoscopic photographs of my models shown in Figs. 5, 25, 28, 30, 45, 49, 50, 88, 92, 95, 96, and 100. For their support and encouragement I am greatly indebted to Mr. A. J. Hailwood (Associate Research Manager) and Mr. J. D. Rose (Research Director) of the Dyestuffs Division of Imperial Chemical Industries Limited.

A. F. W.

CONTENTS

THE VIEWING OF STEREOSCOPIC PHOTOGRAPHS

NUMEROUS models are illustrated in this book by pairs of stereoscopic photographs. At the end of the last century stereoscopic photographs were very popular, and the stereoscope was a familiar object in many homes. Unfortunately this is no longer true, and although it is possible to purchase a simple viewer some readers may prefer to make one. The two photographs of a pair, having been taken from points about $2\frac{1}{2}$ inches apart, correspond to the two views seen by the eyes in normal vision. It is therefore necessary to ensure that each eye sees only the appropriate photograph. This can be arranged by mounting a pair of planoconvex or biconvex lenses with their centres about $2\frac{1}{2}$ inches apart in a piece of opaque material. Suitable lenses would have a diameter of about 1 inch and focal length about 4 inches, and the hardboard, wood, or metal should be shaped so that the viewer may be held close to the eyes. Obvious refinements include mounting the lenses separately and pinning together the two pieces of hardboard so that allowance may be made for variations in the separation of the eyes of different users, and mounting the viewer on light legs (either detachable or hinged so as to fold flat) which will support it at the correct height above the photographs. The constructional details will depend on the materials available, and although a viewer can be made in a matter of minutes by placing two lenses over holes cut in a piece of cardboard it will be found that a viewer of the kind described will be more convenient to use.

CORRIGENDA

Page 15, line 6. *For* unity *read* two

Page 55, 4 lines up. *For* 0·115 *read* 0·155

Plate XVI, Fig. 99 should be
rotated through 180° as a pair

INTRODUCTION

One of the many peculiarities of a human being is that when confronted with a problem or when called upon to make a judgement his behaviour depends on a variety of factors such as the colour of his hair, his religion, the way in which he was educated, his father's income (and his own), and many others. This may seem so self-evident and well known as to require no emphasis here, but the very things which are most obvious are sometimes those which are most easily overlooked, a fact put to good use by G. K. Chesterton in several of his delightful short stories. Alternatively we may say that a person adopts a particular viewpoint depending on his environment and upbringing; he does not view a thing objectively and as a whole but from a particular angle and in part. He subconsciously introduces mental reservations and limitations which are of his own making.

One of the objects of education is to widen the angle of view and make us aware of these reservations and limitations. As a very simple example of an artificial limitation introduced by people when thinking about a problem we may give the childish puzzle in which we are required to draw four straight lines to pass through nine points without lifting the pencil off the paper or passing twice along any line (Fig. 1 (*a*)). Although there is no injunction to keep within the area bounded by the points, the general tendency is to attempt to solve the problem in this way. We are all familiar with the match puzzles in which we are required to form a number of triangles, squares, etc., with a specified number of matches. How many people, when asked to form four equilateral triangles with six matches, think of forming a tetrahedron (Fig. 1 (*b*)), though nothing was said about keeping all the matches in one plane? This brings us to the theme of this book.

From the physical standpoint we live an essentially 2-dimensional existence. We move about the surface of the earth and seldom travel far in a direction perpendicular to the surface. Even the airman has very little vertical freedom compared with the distances he travels over the earth's surface. This is no doubt one reason why we tend to think 'two-dimensionally' rather than 'three-dimensionally', but perhaps an equally important reason is our addiction to flat surfaces, in particular sheets of paper, on which we write and draw pictures. It seems likely that a young child has a better appreciation of the third

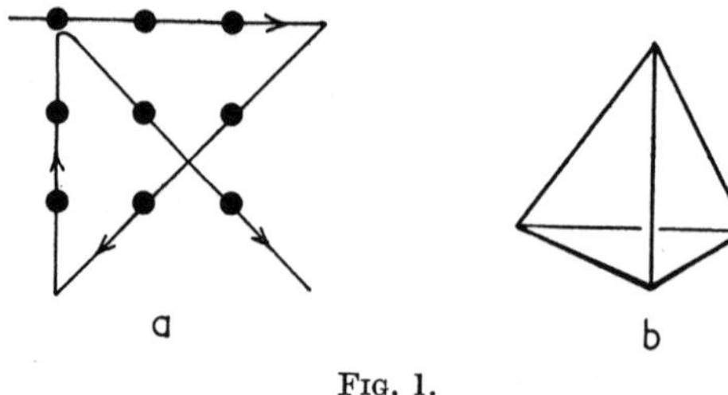

Fig. 1.

dimension before he can read and write than afterwards. He plays with toy bricks, builds 'houses', and falls from chairs or cots. His size is more nearly comparable with the heights of chairs and tables. Later in life he is, or should be, less likely to fall from chairs, an experience which teaches that there is height as well as length and breadth. If it is true that a gradual mental change accompanies the substitution of drawing on paper for making models with bricks or plasticine, this is accentuated by the use of maps, the emphasis on the teaching of plane geometry in schools, and generally by the representation of any solid object by a plane drawing. We become so accustomed to the use of ordinary photographs, from which as the result of experience we can form a fair reconstruction of the original, that it causes something of a shock to view the same scene stereoscopically. Only then do we realize what was lost by the normal method of photography.

There can be great beauty in a pressed flower in a herbarium, but this is small compared with that of the growing plant. The relative dispositions of the various parts have been lost; it has been pressed into two dimensions. Many plants have a characteristic 'attitude', a particular curve of the stem or some angular relationship between a number of stems or between the leaves and stem. Other plants have highly symmetrical arrangements of leaves or petals, as, for example, the heaths shown in Fig. 2.

A map is a sufficiently faithful representation of a small area of the earth's surface and has certain advantages over a globe. However, the use of maps instead of globes, or perhaps the failure to appreciate the limitations of the different projections

FIG. 2. Arrangement of leaves around the stems of *Erica tetralix* L. and *Erica cinerea* L.

used in map-making, can lead to peculiar misconceptions. It is not difficult to see why Greenland appears with different shapes on different maps, but it is surprising that so few people realize that one can travel 10 miles due south, then 10 miles due east, and finally 10 miles due north and arrive back at the starting-point—if only one starts from the North Pole. Still fewer people would, without further thought, perceive that there are also an indefinite number of points close to the South Pole which also satisfy the above condition, namely, all points such as A in Fig. 3 which are 10 miles due north of circles around the South Pole having circumferences of 10 miles or any submultiple of this distance.

It so happens that the British Isles and New Zealand are approximately at opposite ends of a diameter of the earth. On the map of Fig. 4 (Mercator's projection) all the routes shown as curved lines and also the two routes $ABCD$ and $AEFD$ via

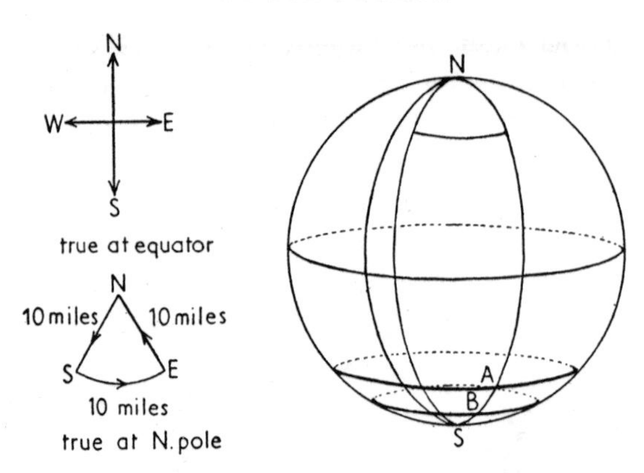

FIG. 3. The points of the compass. The circumference of the small circle through *B* is 10 miles, and the distance *AB* is equal to 10 miles.

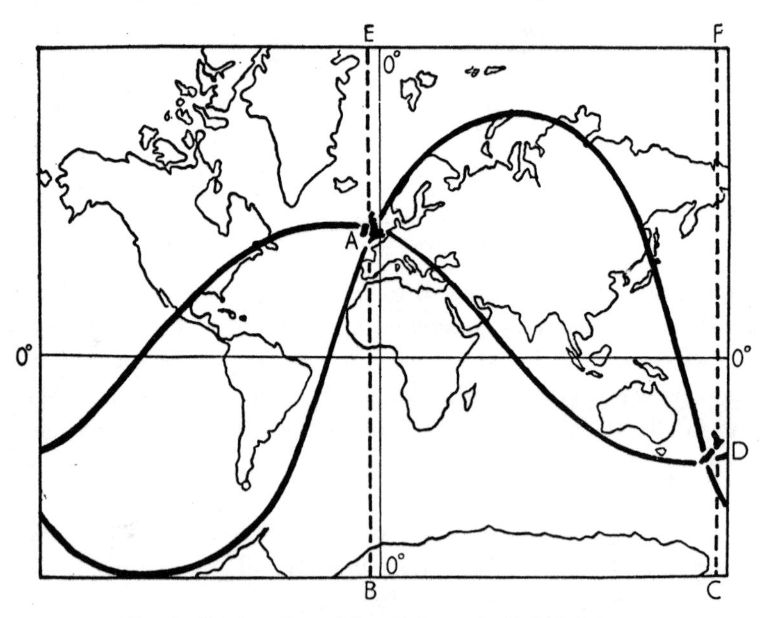

FIG. 4. Routes of equal length from the British Isles to New Zealand (Mercator's Projection).

the Poles are of the same length, all being simply the projections of a set of great circles joining the two points in question.

All this may appear to have little connexion with the title of this book, but in fact it has a great deal to do with it. The chemist is concerned with the properties of atoms—how, and why, and under what conditions they react together to form groups of atoms, and how these new groups behave and can be built into more complex arrangements. One aspect of chemistry is the spatial arrangements of the component atoms in such groups, and this is the subject we are going to discuss. We shall be concerned only with this structural aspect of chemistry in this book, and not at all with such questions as 'Why does one arrangement of atoms form and another not?' or 'What is the chemical behaviour resulting from a particular structure?'

The architect is concerned not only with the materials used in building and with lengths, breadths, and heights, which are determined by the properties of the materials and by the use to which the structure is to be put, but also with other properties of the building as a whole. Apart from aesthetic considerations, there is more in a building than certain numbers of rooms, corridors, and so on of specified dimensions. There are certain relations between the parts of a building which depend on the use to which it is to be put. An architect can visualize a building from a plan and elevations, just as an engineer can mentally reconstruct a piece of machinery from such 2-dimensional drawings. In chemistry we can represent the composition of a substance by a set of symbols showing the numbers of atoms of different kinds, but such a formula gives no hint of the arrangement of the atoms. We can do a little better if we group certain of the atoms together, as in $Na(ClO_3)$, which indicates rather more than $NaClO_3$ but is not so informative as

$$\mathrm{Na}\left[\begin{matrix} \mathrm{O} & & \mathrm{O} \\ & \mathrm{Cl} & \\ & \mathrm{O} & \end{matrix}\right] \quad \text{or better still} \quad \left[\begin{matrix} & \mathrm{Cl} & \\ \mathrm{O} & & \mathrm{O} \\ & \mathrm{O} & \end{matrix}\right]^{-} \mathrm{Na}^{+}.$$

In the last case we have shown that the grouping ClO_3 has the form of a pyramid with the three oxygen atoms at the corners of the triangular base and the chlorine atom raised above the centre. It will be evident that formulae of any type written on paper are very inadequate representations of complex molecules, and for the 3-dimensional arrangements of atoms in crystals even perspective drawings are poor substitutes for models. Insufficient use is made of stereoscopic photographs, which provide the most satisfactory representations of 3-dimensional structures on paper.

The most complex examples of atomic architecture are the structures of living things. The chemist has succeeded in elucidating the structures of relatively small groupings of atoms in compounds such as sugars, alkaloids, and the colouring matters of some flowers, but we are still far from knowing the arrangements of atoms in, say, haemoglobin or wool. A peculiar difficulty arises in many cases from the fact that not only are many natural products very complex as regards their chemical composition but in addition there is only a moderate degree of regularity in the arrangement of the constituent atoms. A high degree of order assists the physicist in determining the structure of a substance, and we know more about the structures of solid substances with highly ordered structures than about those built in a less regular manner.

The most elegant and regular atomic architecture is found in crystals, many of which, particularly those found in Nature as minerals, are objects of great beauty. As we shall have a good deal to say about crystals it will perhaps be advisable to make clear exactly what is meant by a crystal, and this is best done by explaining first what is not a crystal.† The word crystal is associated in many people's minds with natural gem-stones, ornaments, and utensils of cut-glass (e.g. English 'crystal'), or with the spherical objects into which certain individuals gaze with the professed object of foretelling the future. Of these, the transparent natural gem-stones alone are crystals, though

† It is likely that some readers will find it unnecessary to read the following passage, just as others will not need to be reminded of the names of the five regular solids. In a book of this kind this difficulty is not easily overcome. Indeed it is to be hoped that one day the book as a whole will be superfluous, for then the author's object in writing it will have been fulfilled. At present, however, it is still possible to find many otherwise well-educated people who use the adjective 'crystal-clear' without a real understanding of its origin, and others who do not always distinguish meticulously between words such as 'melt' and 'dissolve'.

their shapes are due to the skill of the cutter who has enhanced their brilliance by producing special arrangements of facets. No object made of glass is a crystal, whether it is the prism which used to adorn the Victorian mantelshelf or chandelier, the smaller piece of 'paste' cut to imitate a diamond, or the sphere of the 'crystal-gazer'.

The Greeks used the same word (*krustallos*) for ice, one of the most familiar examples of a crystalline solid, and for quartz (rock-crystal), which is one of the commonest minerals in the earth's crust. Quartz occurs in a variety of forms, as the colourless component of granite, as single crystals which have grown in cavities in rocks (Fig. 5, Plate I), or more familiarly as sandstone or the sand on the sea-shore. The characteristic shape of the colourless, transparent, rock-crystal was known to the ancients, and the study of quartz crystals played an important part in the early development of the science of crystallography, as we shall see in Chapter IV. Fig. 5 also shows some crystals grown in the laboratory; we refer to these at the beginning of Chapter IV.

The reader may well inquire: Why this distinction between a diamond and a piece of glass cut to the same shape? The answer lies in the profound difference between the internal structures of the two materials, a difference which we can illustrate by the following rather crude analogy. If bricks are emptied from a truck they form a pile in which they are arranged in a quite disorderly way (Fig. 6 (*a*)). There are, on the other hand, more regular arrangements possible, such as those shown at (*b*) and (*c*). In a liquid the minute particles of which it is composed are moving about, and at any given moment are arranged quite randomly. When the temperature falls this movement slows down, and in the case of a pure substance the particles usually line up in a regular way like the bricks in (*b*) or (*c*). We say that the substance has crystallized. If the crystals are free to grow separately they form single crystals, as shown diagrammatically at (*d*). If the ordering process takes place simultaneously in many places we obtain the result shown at (*e*). Granite is a rock formed by the solidification of a molten mixture of minerals, and the growth of each individual crystal was impeded by that of its neighbours, leading to irregular shapes as shown in the photograph of a thin section (Fig. 7 (*a*), Plate II). Again, when a mass of molten metal solidifies crystallization begins at numerous places throughout the mass, and each small crystal grows until it meets its neighbours. If the

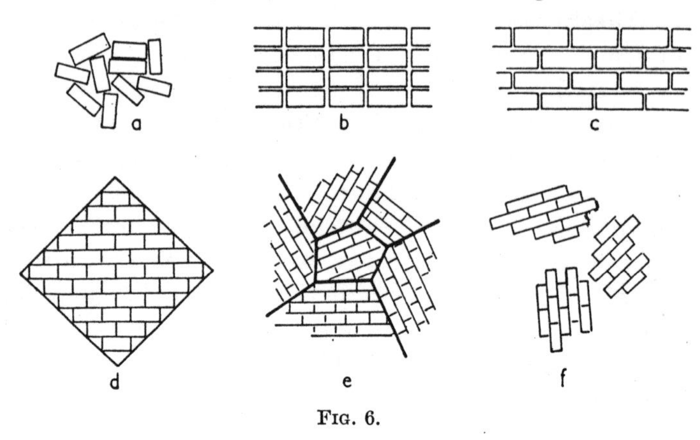

FIG. 6.

surface of such a polycrystalline material is polished and etched the grain boundaries are accentuated (Fig. 7 (*b*), Plate II). An even more elegant way of showing the grain boundaries is to prepare stereoscopic radiographs. The grain boundaries in a sheet of aluminium are made more visible by incorporating a small percentage of tin and then heat-treating the alloy so that the tin, which is less transparent to X-rays than the aluminium, segregates at the boundaries (Fig. 8, Plate II). The familiar forms of metals—block, sheet, and wire—are all polycrystalline, but it is possible to grow single crystals of some metals in the laboratory, and well-developed crystals of some metals are found as minerals.

Suppose now that when the molten material represented by Fig. 6 (*a*) is cooled something interferes with the lining-up process (crystallization) so that the particles become, as it were, 'frozen' into the positions they occupied in the melt. The result is then a glass, or supercooled liquid. Glasses are most readily formed by mixtures, particularly of silicates and borates, but some pure elements and compounds also form glasses under suitable conditions. A special property of glasses that makes them of such value is that they do not, like crystalline substances, melt sharply at a definite temperature. Instead, they soften when heated, that is, the change to the liquid state takes place over a considerable range of temperature, and in this semi-molten condition the glass can be moulded or blown into various shapes. A glass still has a tendency to change into a crystalline solid, though the change (devitrification) may take years or even centuries. It then becomes a polycrystalline mass which is no longer transparent like the original glass.

If a substance in the form of single crystals is ground up we still describe the powder as crystalline (or microcrystalline) for we have merely broken up the single crystals without disturbing the orderly arrangement in the interior of the particles, though these now have quite irregular shapes (Fig. 6 (*f*)). A simple example of this type of change is the grinding of granulated sugar into 'icing' sugar.

Before we go further we should perhaps point out that crystals are not simply objects of academic interest, to be associated in people's minds with laboratories or museums. Snowflakes consist of water which has crystallized into rather complex shapes instead of compact crystals, but even more familiar examples of crystalline substances are common salt and granulated sugar. If we look at some grains of ordinary table salt through a magnifying glass (or preferably a simple microscope), we see that they are all very similar in shape and are either cubes or rectangular blocks. If the crystals had grown under ideal conditions all would be perfect cubes. If granulated sugar is examined in the same way we find again that each particle is a little crystal with a characteristic shape, very much like its neighbours but quite different from those of salt. Other examples of common crystals are washing-soda, bath-salts, and photographer's hypo. The faces on the pea-sized crystals of hypo are easily visible to the naked eye, but the sizes of crystals range from the inches or feet of some natural crystals to dimensions so small that the shapes of the crystals are recognizable only when they have been magnified many thousands of times. The white smoke of magnesium oxide formed when magnesium ribbon is burned (the flashlight of the photographer) consists of beautifully formed crystals, but their shapes are distinguishable only in the electron microscope, under a magnification of many thousand times (Fig. 9 (*a*), Plate III).

We shall not discuss in this book the practical importance of crystals or of the process of crystallization. It is not difficult to appreciate that the properties of metals and alloys will depend not only on the arrangement of the atoms within the individual crystals but also on the 'texture' of the polycrystalline material. It is perhaps worth while to note here a few examples which at first sight might not appear to have much to do with crystals at all. Photographic plates and films owe their properties to the minute crystals of silver salts embedded in a gelatine layer. These crystals are sensitive to light, and crystals on which light has fallen are developable to grains of metallic silver in the developing bath. A highly magnified photograph of a photographic film (Fig. 9 (*b*), Plate III) shows the characteristic shapes of silver halide crystals. In the cathode-ray tube, with which we are all familiar in this television age, the image is formed on a layer of finely crystalline material sensitive to electrons which are released from the electron-gun situated near the opposite end of the tube.

Large single crystals of quartz are used for stabilizing the wavelengths of radio transmitters, and were also used at first in coaxial circuits for long-distance telephony. Several hundreds of telephone calls can be carried by one such circuit, each conversation being guided along its assigned frequency channel by a filter based on a single crystal of quartz, or more recently ethylene diamine tartrate. Quartz clocks are used as time standards at the Royal Observatory and to control the broadcast time signals and the 'talking clock' of the telephone service. The basis of such a clock is a small quartz crystal which is maintained in oscillation by a valve circuit and vibrates some 100,000 times a second, keeping the rate of the clock constant to within one thousandth part of a second a day. (This is not the accuracy of the *time* recorded by such a clock, for time is defined in terms of the period of rotation of the earth on its axis, and the *rate* of the clock must be checked by astronomical observations.)

The 'jewels' in watches and the bearings in many scientific instruments consist of rubies or sapphires, both of which are crystalline aluminium oxide coloured by different impurities. Nowadays colourless synthetic sapphire is used, being prepared by crystallizing alumina after it has been melted in an oxy-hydrogen flame.

More mundane examples of the importance of crystallization are to be found in processes such as the setting of plaster and cement. These depend on the growth, from solution, of inter-locking crystals on which the strength of the resulting material depends. In this case crystal growth is required; in others it has to be avoided. For example, the pigments in paints are usually finely ground crystalline materials, and the covering power of the paint depends on the shape and size of the particles. If appreciable growth of the crystals occurred during storage the paint would become useless. We see therefore that crystals enter, in one way or another, into many branches of science and technology, and it is perhaps as well that we should emphasize here the practical importance of crystallography since we shall make no further reference to this aspect of the subject.

We shall have more to say about the shapes of crystals later, for the study of the arrangement of the faces on crystals laid the foundations for the later studies of their internal structures. These, however, had to wait for a series of discoveries in physics around the end of the nineteenth century, notably the discovery of X-rays (1895), radioactivity (1896), and the electron (1897), which rapidly led to the modern theory of the structure of the atom. Before we consider crystals in any detail we shall discuss some geometrical topics which form the natural introduction to our subject.

CHAPTER I

POLYGONS AND PLANE NETS

From Polygons to Phyllotaxis

WHEN described as a plane figure enclosed by a number of lines a polygon does not sound a very attractive or interesting object. However, the polygon forms a natural starting-point for our study of atomic architecture since we shall be interested in all kinds of patterns formed from polygons. Polygons are of various kinds. First, we may distinguish two groups, concave and convex polygons. If any vertex lies inside the line joining the vertices on each side of it there is a re-entrant angle. A convex polygon is one which has no re-entrant angles. The 'star' polygons, formed by extending outwards the edges of the regular polygons until pairs meet, are a set of very symmetrical non-convex polygons. For the time being we shall be concerned only with plane, convex polygons, which can have any number of sides from three upwards. (If we permit curved sides we can have also a digon with two sides.) After the triangle and quadrilateral there is a systematic nomenclature, pentagon (5), hexagon (6), etc., and there are also a number of trivial names for special types of quadrilateral, namely, trapezium, parallelogram, rhombus, rectangle, and square. We shall often refer to larger polygons as 10-gons, etc., to avoid too great a strain on our knowledge of Greek.

A special group of convex polygons have all their sides and angles equal; these are the regular polygons, and they can obviously be generated by repeating one vertex at regular intervals around a central point (Fig. 10 (*a*)). For a polygon of n sides (e.g. 5) we rotate the line OA_1 around O through $360°/5 = 72°$ to obtain successive vertices A_2, A_3, etc. The imaginary line through O about which we have rotated the line OA_1 is called an axis of n-fold (here 5-fold) symmetry. (We shall have more to say about symmetry in a later chapter in connexion with the shapes of crystals.) From this method of constructing a regular polygon it follows that all its vertices lie on a circle, the circumscribing circle. We could alternatively take a line at right angles to the radial line and rotate this through $360°/n$. Now the points B_1, B_2, etc., lie on a circle (inscribed circle) to which the edges of the polygon are tangents at these points, the mid-points of the edges (Fig. 10 (*b*)). The existence of these two

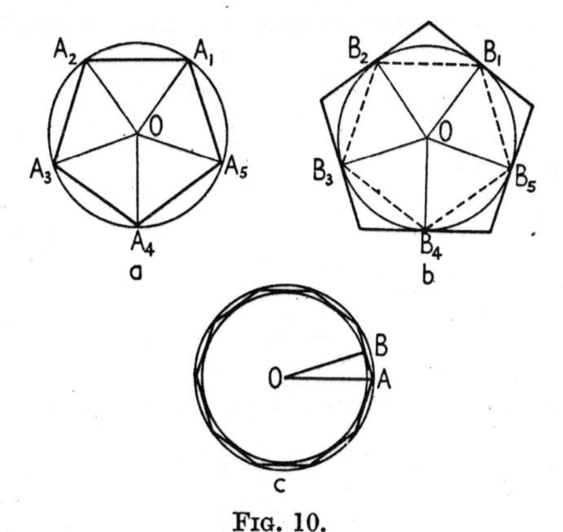

FIG. 10.

circles suggests a way of finding the value of π, the ratio of the circumference of a circle to its diameter. As the number of edges of the polygon increases so the inscribed and circumscribed circles approach closer one to the other and the perimeter of the polygon approximates more closely to a circle (Fig. 10 (*c*)). So also the ratios of the perimeter to AO and to BO approach, from opposite directions, the value of 2π:

	Number of sides			
	6	*12*	*30*	*60*
perimeter/AO . .	6·000	6·211	6·270	6·276
perimeter/BO . .	6·929	6·431	6·306	6·288

$$2\pi = 6{\cdot}2832$$

Archimedes estimated the value of 2π in this way from the polygon with 96 sides.

The dependence on π of the areas of the surfaces and volumes of figures of revolution is well known: for example, area of circle πr^2, volume of sphere $4\pi r^3/3$, volume of cone $\pi r^2 h/3$. It is interesting to digress here to mention another number τ, which is related to certain polygons and polyhedra. In a regular pentagon with sides one unit in length the length of the diagonal is τ, which like π is an irrational number ($\tau = 1{\cdot}61803...$). From the angles of the regular pentagon it is evident that $\tau = 2\cos\pi/5$. The same number occurs as the distance from the centre to a vertex of a regular decagon of side one unit in length (Fig. 11).

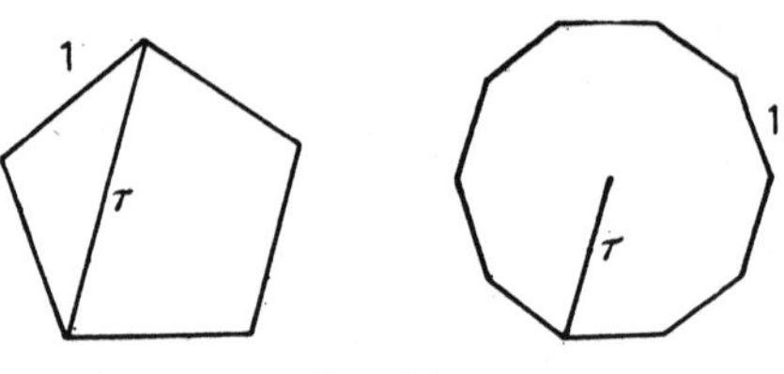

FIG. 11.

The number τ satisfies (or is the positive root of) the equation

$$\tau^2-\tau-1 = 0$$

whence
$$\tau = \frac{1+\sqrt{5}}{2}$$

and from which it follows, for example, that

$$\frac{\tau}{1} = \frac{1}{\tau-1} = \frac{\tau-1}{2-\tau}, \quad \text{etc.}$$

A line is said to be divided in the Golden Section if the ratio of its parts is τ. The self-explanatory Fig. 12 shows Euclid's construction. From the fact that $\tau = 1/(\tau-1)$ it is evident that if we have a rectangle whose sides are τ and 1, then after cutting off a square we are left with a rectangle of the same proportions as the original. This process may be continued indefinitely, the sides of the rectangles being the numerators and denominators of

$$\frac{\tau}{1} = \frac{1}{\tau-1} = \frac{\tau-1}{2-\tau}, \quad \text{etc.}$$

If we take three rectangular cards with sides in the ratio $\tau:1$ and cut slots so that they may be placed together as shown in Fig. 13 we find that the twelve corners of the cards are the vertices of one of the regular solids, which we shall describe in

Chapter II. This one is the icosahedron, the faces of which are twenty equilateral triangles. It is interesting to note the connexion of τ with the regular 5- and 10-gons; this number also enters into the formulae for the surface areas and volumes of

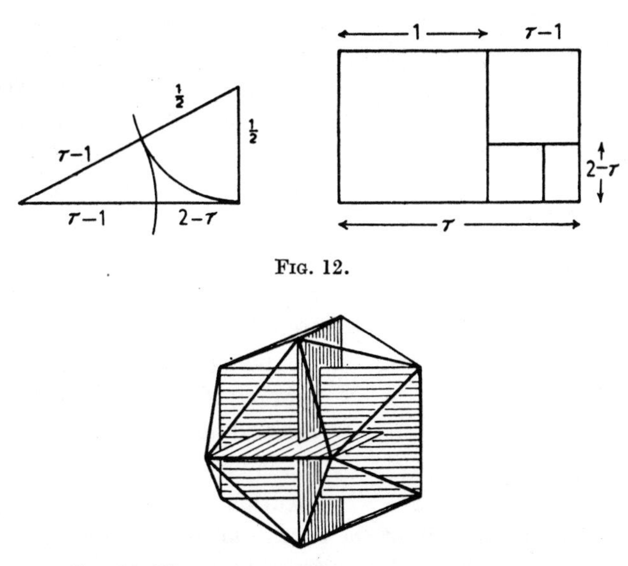

FIG. 12.

FIG. 13. The card edges which become edges of the icosahedron are those of unit length.

the regular dodecahedron and icosahedron, their volumes being $4\sqrt{5}\tau^4$ and $20\tau^2/3$ respectively if the length of an edge is unity.

From τ it is tempting to digress just a little further from polygons to a series of numbers named after Leonardo of Pisa, also called Fibonacci, who investigated them in the thirteenth century. Starting with two 1's each successive number is the sum of the two preceding numbers, so that there is no need to memorize more than the first two numbers. The ratios of alternate pairs of successive numbers approach τ, the upper series of ratios increasing towards the value 1·61803... and the lower series decreasing towards the same number.

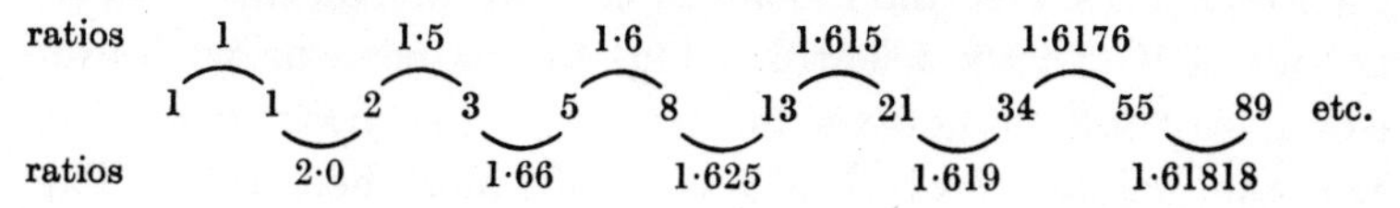

Phyllotaxis

This subject is concerned with the arrangement of leaves around the stems of plants, of the scales on fir-cones, or the florets in the central inflorescences of daisies, sunflowers, and the like. If we examine a fir-cone we find that the woody scales are arranged in lines running up the cone in a sort of helical path. Each scale lies on, and at the intersection of, two such lines, one going up from right to left (*a*) and the other from left to right (*b*) in Fig. 14. In this diagram the fir-cone (or branch) is regarded as cylindrical and unwrapped to form a plane surface, the numbers indicating the scales (or leaves)—compare the projection of the earth's surface in Fig. 4.

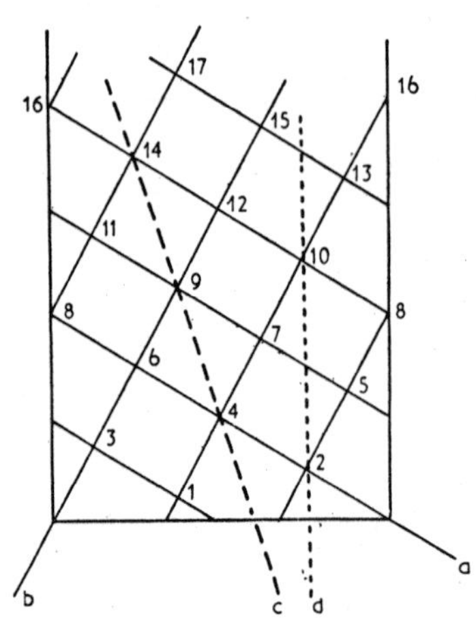

FIG. 14. Arrangement of scales on a fir-cone (diagrammatic).

The numbers of lines of type (*a*) and (*b*) are different and they differ on cones of different families of trees. The numbers of helical lines can also be counted on the central disks of daisies and sunflowers, and some typical figures are:

	Numbers of helices	
	a	*b*
Cypress	2	3
Norway spruce	3	5
Scotch fir, larch	5	8
Daisy	13	21
Sunflowers	34	55
	55	89

It will be noted that these are pairs of successive numbers in the Fibonacci series, and much has been written on this subject, not all of it strictly scientific. Fig. 14 has been drawn as an example of 2:3 phyllotaxis, but we could have drawn lines such as *c*, the number of which is 5, or *d*, of which there are 8. The choice of a special pair of Fibonacci numbers to describe a particular cone is therefore arbitrary in so far as the eye notices the most conspicuous lines of scales. A very readable account of this subject is available in D'Arcy Thompson's *On Growth and Form.*

Division of a Plane into Polygons

From the isolated polygon we turn to groups of polygons. It is obviously possible to divide any polygon into any number of smaller polygons. At (*a*) in Fig. 15 we have divided a penta-

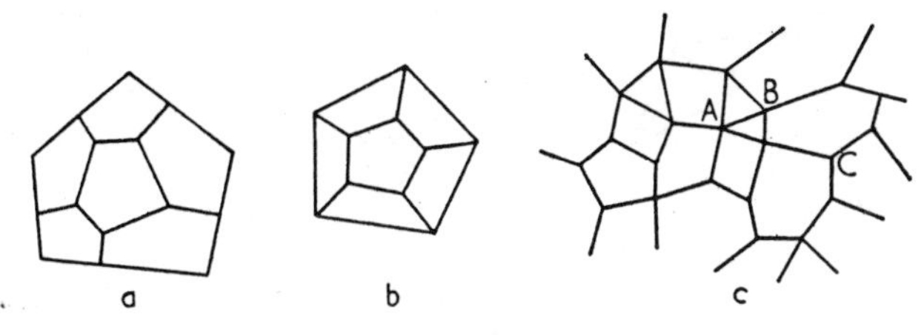

FIG. 15.

gon into six smaller pentagons; at (*b*) into five quadrilaterals and a pentagon. It is also evident that we could divide any plane surface, of finite or indefinite extent, into polygons, and the same is true of any closed surface such as that of a sphere or cylinder. However, we are not interested in haphazard arrangements of polygons, and to find the rules governing these systems we shall start with plane surfaces of indefinite extent and then proceed to closed surfaces in the next chapter.

In Fig. 15 (*c*) we have drawn at random a system of lines dividing part of a plane surface into polygons. We notice first that the polygons have different numbers of sides and second that different numbers of lines meet at points such as *A*, *B*, and *C*. It is apparent that at least three lines must meet at each point in order to avoid re-entrant angles. We could therefore immediately introduce one simplification, namely, that the same number of lines meet at every point, this number being three, four, five, etc. Alternatively, or in addition, we could stipulate that all the polygons are to have the same number of sides. We shall find that if we introduce both of these restrictions simultaneously very few arrangements of polygons are possible.

Let us start by considering a set of points P_i in number enclosed by a convex polygon R having P_r vertices (Fig. 16 (*a*)). Join up the outer points P_r with the inner ones and the latter

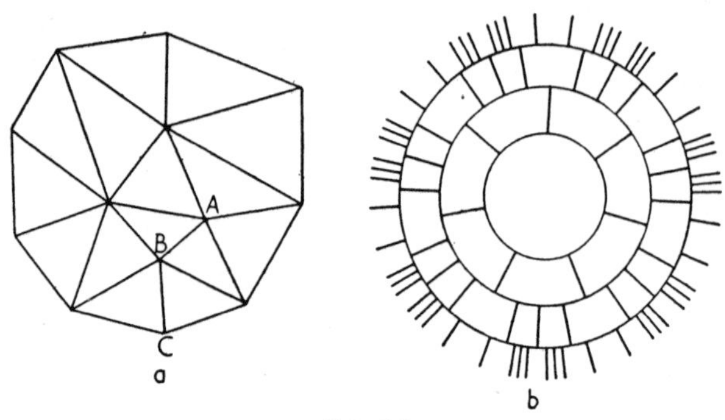

FIG. 16.

among themselves, so that the whole becomes a system of triangles. The sum of the interior angles of the convex polygon with P_r vertices is $180°\ (P_r-2)$. Around each inner point the sum of the angles is 360°, so that the sum of all the angles within R is equal to $180°\ (P_r+2P_i-2)$. Since the sum of the interior angles of a triangle is equal to 180° it follows that the number of triangles is P_r+2P_i-2.

We can imagine P_i made as large as we like compared with P_r so that when n, the total number of points, is very large P_r/P_i tends to zero. (Actually there are other ways of dividing a plane into polygons all of which are surrounded in the same way so that, for example, all are 7-gons, 8-gons, etc., but for $n \geqslant 7$ the value of P_r/P_i does not converge to zero. An example is shown in Fig. 16 (*b*): for this radiating system of 7-gons the limiting value of P_r/P_i is $(1+\sqrt{5})/2$, a number we have already met as the value of τ.) The number of triangles is then $2P_i$, since P_r-2 can be neglected, i.e. any indefinitely extended system of points (n in number) can be connected up to form a system of $2n$ triangles. (There is apparently no corresponding rule for a *3*-dimensional array of points. For example, if such a system of n_∞ points is joined up to form an_∞ tetrahedra there is no unique value of a.)

Since each triangle has three sides and each side is common to two triangles, the number of edges in our assembly of triangles is $3n$:

$$\left.\begin{array}{l} n \text{ points} \\ 3n \text{ edges} \\ 2n \text{ triangles} \end{array}\right\} \quad (A)$$

We now wish to find the corresponding quantities for any assembly of polygons *of all kinds* in which three edges meet at every point. Since each edge joins two points and three edges meet at each point there must be $3n/2$ edges in a system of n points. The problem is to determine the total number of polygons.

If we remove one edge from the assembly of polygons the number of polygons falls by one. Therefore, to change from the assembly of triangles (A) with $3n$ edges to our assembly of polygons with $3n/2$ edges we have to remove $3n/2$ edges and in so doing we remove the same number of polygons. Hence the number of polygons must be $n/2$, since there were $2n$ polygons (triangles) in (A). We have therefore:

$$\left.\begin{array}{l} n \text{ points} \\ 3n/2 \text{ edges} \\ n/2 \text{ polygons} \end{array}\right\} \begin{array}{l} \text{for a 3-connected array of} \\ \text{polygons.} \end{array}$$

For 4-, 5-, and 6-connected systems there must be respectively $2n$, $5n/2$, and $3n$ edges, and comparing with (A) we find:

$$\left.\begin{array}{l} n \text{ points} \\ 2n \text{ edges} \\ n \text{ polygons} \end{array}\right\} \qquad \left.\begin{array}{l} n \text{ points} \\ 5n/2 \text{ edges} \\ 3n/2 \text{ polygons} \end{array}\right\} \qquad \left.\begin{array}{l} n \text{ points} \\ 3n \text{ edges} \\ 2n \text{ polygons} \end{array}\right\}$$

for 4-connected, 5-connected, and 6-connected nets.

We may now derive a general equation for 3-connected plane nets. Let p_k be the fraction of the total number of polygons which are k-gons and therefore $p_k(n/2)$ the actual number of k-gons. If we add up terms

$$3p_3(n/2)+4p_4(n/2)+\ldots kp_k(n/2)$$

we shall count each edge twice (since each is common to two polygons), therefore

$$n/2(3p_3+4p_4+5p_5+...kp_k) = 2(3n/2)$$

or $$3p_3+4p_4+5p_5+...kp_k = 6. \quad (1)$$

For 4-, 5-, and 6-connected nets the corresponding values of $\sum kp_k$† are found in the same way to be 4, 10/3, and 3.

A special solution of equation (1) is

$$p_6 = 1,$$

i.e. all the polygons are hexagons. It also follows from this equation that if we have some polygons with more than six sides then there must also be some with fewer than six sides. For example, the next simplest possibilities are

$$p_5 = \tfrac{1}{2}; \quad p_7 = \tfrac{1}{2}$$

$$p_4 = \tfrac{1}{2}; \quad p_8 = \tfrac{1}{2}$$

and $$p_3 = \tfrac{1}{2}; \quad p_9 = \tfrac{1}{2}.$$

Some of the simplest 3-connected plane nets are illustrated, in their most symmetrical forms, in Fig. 17, but it should be noted that although they have been drawn with regular polygons this is not necessary, for equation (1) is concerned only with the numbers of sides in the polygons. The branch of mathematics dealing with this kind of relation is called topology ('rubber-sheet geometry'). It is concerned with the way in which points are connected, and not at all with such matters as lengths and angles and the straightness or otherwise of the connecting lines. We could, for example, draw the hexagonal net with quite irregular hexagons or with hexagons having sides of different lengths, as in Fig. 18 (*a*). The pattern of Net 1 in Fig. 17 will be recognized as that of wire netting, and that of Fig. 18 (*b*) as one arrangement of bricks in a wall.

There is obviously no limit to the number of solutions of equation (1). In the examples of Fig. 17 there are only two

† The Greek letter Σ (capital sigma) is a convenient shorthand notation for the sum of all terms of a similar kind, in this case those on the left-hand side of equation (1). A particular net contains only certain kinds of polygons; for example, Net 14 of Table 1 (p. 22) consists of 4-gons, 6-gons, and 8-gons. For this net $\sum kp_k$ stands for $4p_4+6p_6+8p_8$.

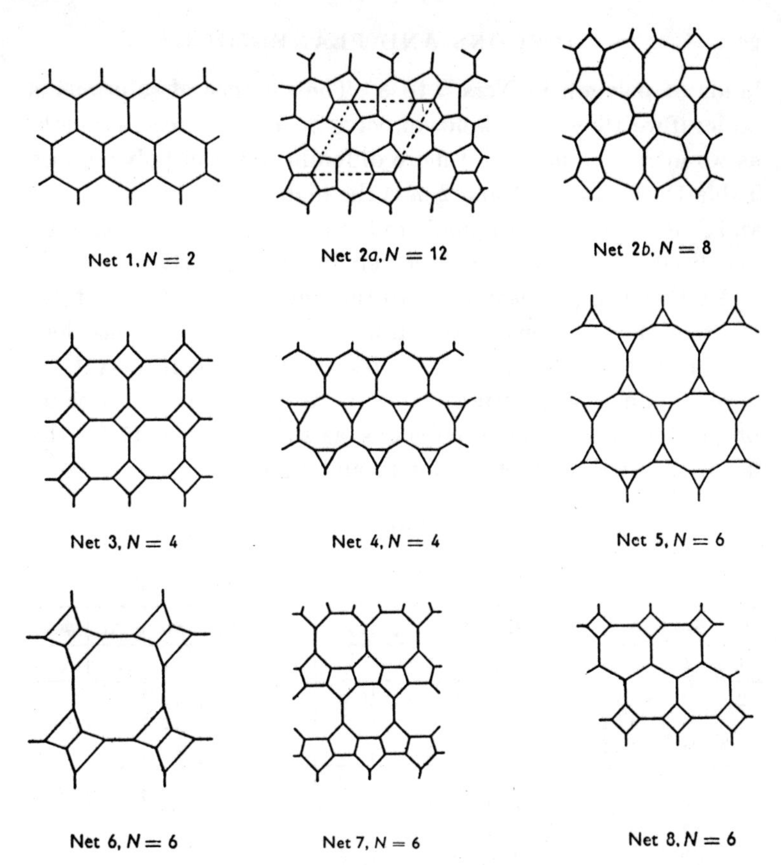

FIG. 17. Some 3-connected plane nets.

N is the number of points in the repeat unit of the pattern (see p. 43).

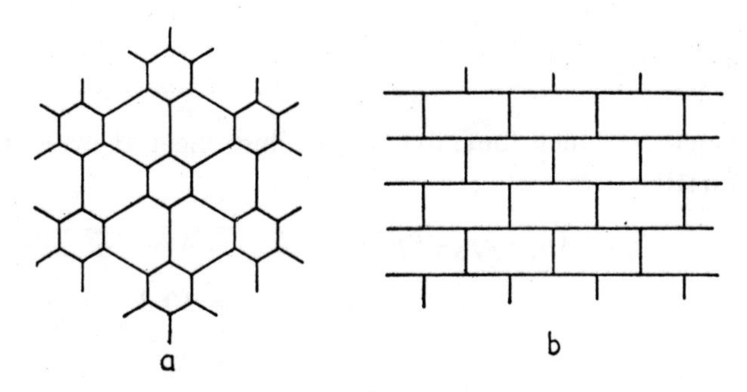

FIG. 18. Forms of the plane hexagonal net.

kinds of polygon in Nets 2 to 8. The number of solutions is larger if we allow three kinds of polygon and it increases rapidly as we introduce more and more different kinds of polygon (see Table 1). In Tables 1 and 2 m is the highest denominator of p_k and N is the number of points in the repeat unit of the pattern. We discuss this aspect of these nets in Chapter III.

Another complication adds to the number of nets. A statement of the fractions of the different kinds of polygons does not in all cases completely specify the net. There may be a number of nets with different relative arrangements of the same proportions and kinds of polygons, as shown in Fig. 17 for the net with equal numbers of 5-gons and 7-gons.

TABLE 1

3-connected Plane Nets

m	*Net*	N	p_3	p_4	p_5	p_6	p_7	p_8	p_9	p_{10}	p_{11}	p_{12}
1	1	2	..	..	..	1	..	..	..	..	..	..
2	2	8, 12	..	..	$\frac{1}{2}$	..	$\frac{1}{2}$	..	..	..	..	..
	3	4	..	$\frac{1}{2}$	..	..	..	$\frac{1}{2}$	..	..	..	..
	4	4	$\frac{1}{2}$	..	..	..	..	..	$\frac{1}{2}$	..	..	..
3	5	6	$\frac{2}{3}$	..	..	..	..	..	..	..	..	$\frac{1}{3}$
	6	6	..	$\frac{2}{3}$	..	..	..	..	..	$\frac{1}{3}$	..	..
	7	6	..	..	$\frac{2}{3}$	..	..	$\frac{1}{3}$	..	..	..	..
	8	6	..	$\frac{1}{3}$	..	..	$\frac{2}{3}$	..	..	..	..	..
	9	6	$\frac{1}{3}$	$\frac{1}{3}$	..	..	..	..	..	..	$\frac{1}{3}$	..
	10	6	$\frac{1}{3}$	..	$\frac{1}{3}$	..	..	..	..	$\frac{1}{3}$	..	..
	11	12	$\frac{1}{3}$	..	..	$\frac{1}{3}$	..	..	$\frac{1}{3}$	..	..	..
	12	6	$\frac{1}{3}$	..	..	..	$\frac{1}{3}$	$\frac{1}{3}$	..	..	..	..
	13	12	..	$\frac{1}{3}$	$\frac{1}{3}$	..	..	..	$\frac{1}{3}$	..	..	..
	14	6	..	$\frac{1}{3}$	..	$\frac{1}{3}$	..	$\frac{1}{3}$	..	..	..	..
	15	12	..	..	$\frac{1}{3}$	$\frac{1}{3}$	$\frac{1}{3}$	..	..	..	..	..

For nets in which four, five, or six lines meet at every point the equations are

$$3p_3+4p_4+5p_5+6p_6+...+kp_k = 4 \quad (2)$$

$$= 10/3 \quad (3)$$

$$= 3. \quad (4)$$

For the 4-connected nets the simplest solution is clearly $p_4 = 1$, i.e. all the polygons are quadrilaterals, and the next simplest solutions are

$$p_3 = \tfrac{1}{2}; \quad p_5 = \tfrac{1}{2},$$

$$p_3 = \tfrac{1}{3}; \quad p_4 = \tfrac{1}{3}; \quad p_5 = \tfrac{1}{3}$$

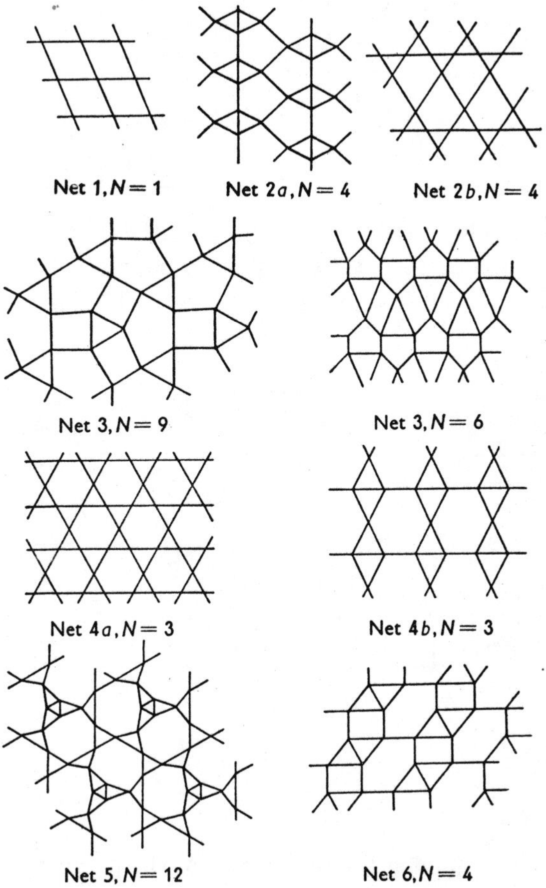

Net 1, $N = 1$ Net 2a, $N = 4$ Net 2b, $N = 4$

Net 3, $N = 9$ Net 3, $N = 6$

Net 4a, $N = 3$ Net 4b, $N = 3$

Net 5, $N = 12$ Net 6, $N = 4$

FIG. 19. Some 4-connected plane nets.

and so on. Some of the simplest 4-connected plane nets are illustrated in Fig. 19 and listed in Table 2.

For arrangements of polygons in which five lines meet at each point the simplest solution of equation (3) is

$$p_3 = \tfrac{2}{3}; \quad p_4 = \tfrac{1}{3}.$$

TABLE 2

4-connected Plane Nets

m	*Net*	N	p_3	p_4	p_5	p_6	p_7
1	1	1	..	1	..	..	..
2	2	4	$\frac{1}{2}$	..	$\frac{1}{2}$	..	..
3	3	6, 9	$\frac{1}{3}$	$\frac{1}{3}$	$\frac{1}{3}$	..	..
	4	3	$\frac{2}{3}$	..	..	$\frac{1}{3}$	..
4	5	12	$\frac{3}{4}$	..	..	..	$\frac{1}{4}$
	6	4	$\frac{1}{2}$	$\frac{1}{4}$	..	$\frac{1}{4}$	..

There is no solution with all polygons of the same type or with simpler fractions than thirds. Two forms of the net, $p_3 = \frac{2}{3}$, $p_4 = \frac{1}{3}$, are shown in Fig. 20 (*a*) and (*b*). The inverse of (*b*),

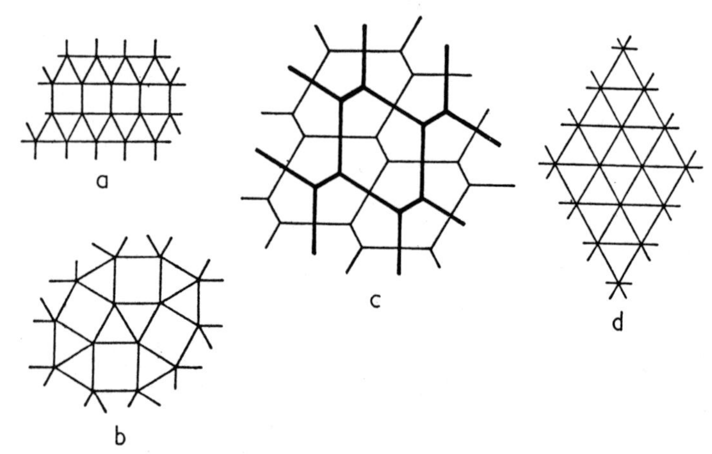

FIG. 20.

resulting from joining the mid-points of the polygons, is a very elegant arrangement of pentagons which has the further point of interest that it can be obtained by superposing two hexagonal nets in the way shown in Fig. 20 (*c*).

When we come to 6-connected nets we find only one solution of equation (4), namely, $p_3 = 1$, the triangular net of Fig. 20 (*d*). Plane arrangements of polygons in which seven or more lines meet in every point are not possible. If we make more than six lines meet in some points then we find fewer than six meeting in others, just as we found that if in the 3-connected nets we have polygons with more than six sides then we must also have polygons with fewer than six sides. We shall find somewhat

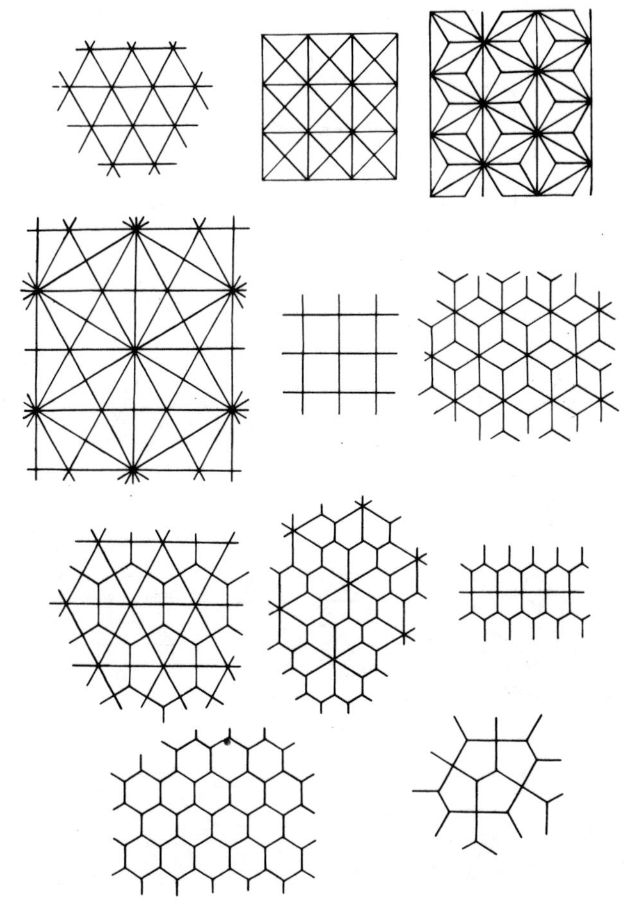

FIG. 21. The division of a plane into congruent convex polygons.

similar restrictions when we come to divide a *closed* surface into polygons.

In deriving these plane nets we have focused our attention on the points, insisting that a certain number of lines should meet at each point. We find an indefinitely large number of arrangements for 3-, 4-, and 5-connected nets, though the number for a given degree of complexity (as expressed by the denominator of the fraction p_k) falls rapidly as we go from 3- to 5-connected nets and finally we find only one 6-connected net.

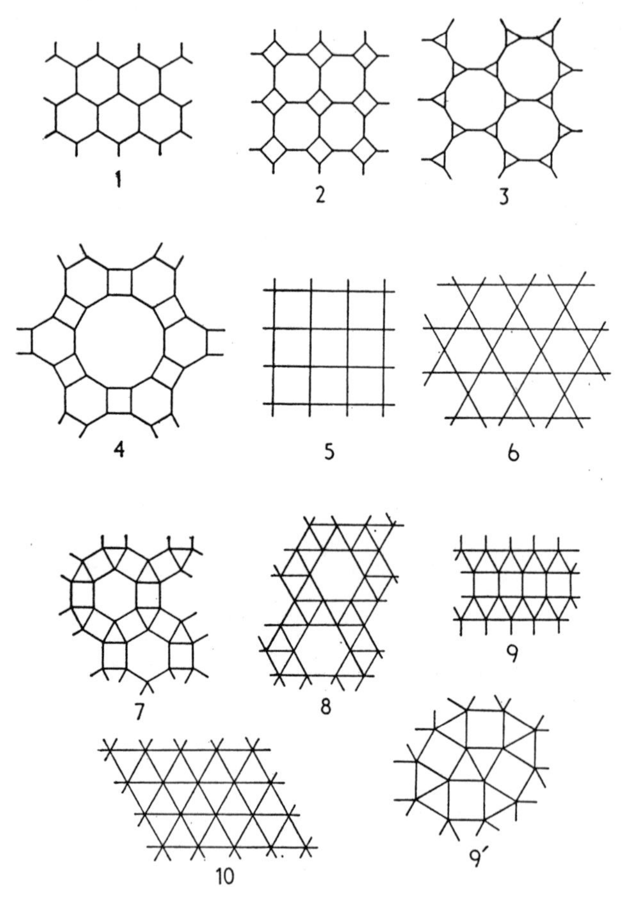

Fig. 22. The division of a plane into regular polygons.

Suppose now that we turn our attention to the polygons instead of the points and ask

(1) In how many ways can a plane surface, of indefinite extent, be divided into congruent convex polygons, i.e.

polygons which are exactly similar as regards shape and size (but not necessarily having the same orientation)?

or (2) In how many ways can a plane surface be divided into *regular* polygons, not necessarily all having the same number of sides?

In both cases it is found that the number of solutions is strictly limited; in fact the answer to both questions is eleven. Moreover, the two sets of plane nets are related in a very simple way, indeed, in the way we have already illustrated in Fig. 20 (*b*) and (*c*). The net of Fig. 20 (*b*) is one of the nets of the second group, consisting of regular polygons (in this instance squares and equilateral triangles), and that of Fig. 20 (*c*) is one of the nets of the first group composed entirely of congruent polygons (pentagons). The complete answers to (1) and (2) are shown in Figs. 21 and 22. Each net in Fig. 21 has been drawn as the reciprocal of the corresponding net in Fig. 22. It should be noted that because the nets of Fig. 21 have been drawn in this way some are shown with *regular* polygons, though the only requirement is that all the polygons are congruent. For example, the net in Fig. 21 corresponding to Net 5 of Fig. 22 is shown as a system of squares; the polygon here could be any parallelogram.

CHAPTER II

POLYHEDRA

Division of a Closed Surface into Polygons: the Regular Solids

We have seen that the division of a plane surface into a repeating pattern of convex polygons is subject to certain rules. The polygons may be all triangles, all quadrilaterals, all pentagons, or all hexagons, but we cannot divide a plane into convex polygons with more than six sides. Or, if we insist that three polygons meet at every point and that all the polygons are to have the same number of sides, then they must be hexagons. Again, if we permit only equilateral triangles there is one arrangement only, that in which six triangles meet at each point. We now wish to know what are the corresponding rules for closed surfaces. Since it is immaterial whether the sides of our polygons are straight or curved we could work on the surface of a sphere. This is convenient from the practical standpoint but difficult to illustrate on paper. However, let us suppose that we have a number of points on the surface of a sphere connected by (curved) lines to form a system of polygons. If we replace each line on the sphere by the straight line lying within the sphere our polygons with curved sides simply become the faces of a solid figure, or polyhedron with straight edges.

Now suppose that this polyhedron is resting on one of its faces and is viewed from below, and let us exaggerate the perspective so that all the other faces appear to lie within the one nearest the observer, as shown for a cube in Fig. 23. The effect is to see the cube as shown at the right. This type of diagram, called a Schlegel diagram, is a very convenient way of representing any polyhedron as a system of polygons all lying within one polygon which is one face of the solid. The correct relative arrangements of all the faces are, of course, retained.

This suggests a method of studying the possible ways of joining up polygons to form closed systems, or polyhedra. For example, to find the polyhedra whose faces are all triangles we have to divide a triangle into a set of smaller triangles. Of the numerous ways in which this can be done three are of special interest in having the same number of faces (or edges) meeting

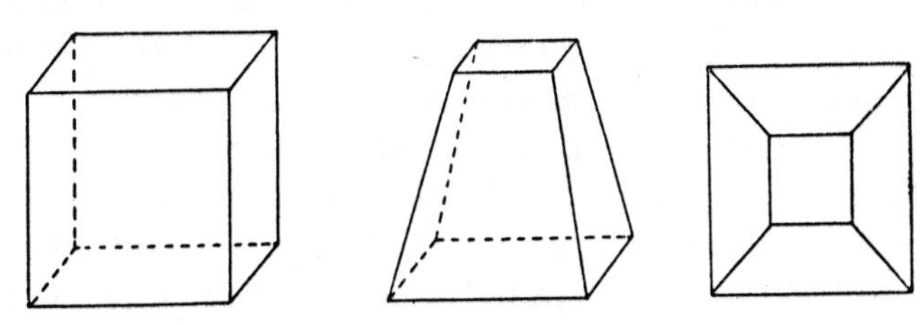

Fig. 23. The Schlegel diagram.

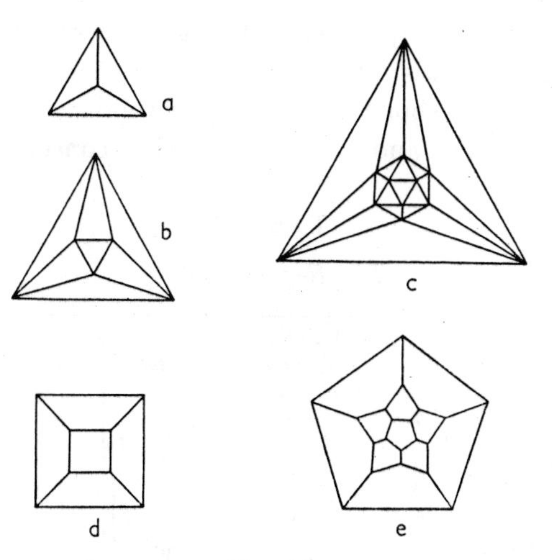

Fig. 24.

at each vertex of the polyhedron (Fig. 24 (*a*)–(*c*)). The first, the tetrahedron, has four triangular faces, three meeting at each vertex. (Four is, of course, the minimum number of faces which can form a closed figure.) The second, the octahedron, has eight triangular faces, four meeting at each of the six vertices, and the third, the icosahedron, has twenty such faces, of which five meet at each of the twelve vertices. If the faces of these polyhedra are *equilateral* triangles these are three of the five *regular* solids, about which we shall have more to say shortly.

Starting with a quadrilateral we should find only one way of dividing it into quadrilaterals if we wish to have the same number of faces meeting at each vertex. The most symmetrical form of the polyhedron represented by Fig. 24 (*d*) is the cube, another of the regular solids. We should find only one way of dividing a pentagon into pentagons such that the same number meet at each vertex (Fig. 24 (*e*)). This Schlegel diagram represents a solid with twenty vertices and twelve faces (pentagons). If the faces are regular pentagons it is the regular dodecahedron, the last regular solid. If we started with a hexagon, or in fact with any polygon having more than five sides, we should find it impossible to divide it into polygons of the same kind if all the vertices are to be equivalent. In other words, there are no further regular solids. A very simple and elegant proof of this fact will be given shortly. The regular solids are illustrated in Fig. 25, Plate IV, and some information concerning them is given in Table 3.

TABLE 3

The Regular Solids

	Type of face (n-gon)	*Number of edges meeting at each vertex*	*Total number of edges*	*Number of faces*	*Number of vertices*
Tetrahedron	3	3	6	4	4
Octahedron	3	4	12	8	6
Cube	4	3		6	8
Dodecahedron	5	3	30	12	20
Icosahedron	3	5		20	12

A polyhedron is described as *isohedral* if all its faces are alike and *isogonal* if all its corners are alike (i.e. the same number and arrangement of faces meet at each). The regular solids have all their faces regular and alike and all their vertices surrounded in the same manner. If it seems remarkable that only five such solids are possible it is perhaps even more remarkable that this fact was known to the ancients. An Etruscan dodecahedron was unearthed in excavations on Monte Loffa, near Padua, showing that this solid was known at least 2,500 years ago. Plato built the five regular solids (about 400 B.C.) by sticking together polygons, and they had probably been made before by the earliest Pythagoreans. A little experimenting will show that four of the regular solids are more easily constructed than the regular dodecahedron. The icosahedron, apparently the most difficult, can be made from a pentagonal antiprism (see p. 34) plus a pyramid on both the bases, whereas the regular dodecahedron has to be made by placing five pentagons around a central pentagon and forming these into a sort of bowl, and joining two such bowls together. A certain Timaeus of Locri therefore suggested a mystical correspondence between the four easily constructed solids and the four natural 'elements' (earth, air, fire, and water). 'Undeterred by the occurrence of a fifth (regular) solid he regarded the dodecahedron as a shape that envelops the whole universe.'†

The following is a version of Euclid's proof that there can be only five regular solids. Let the faces be polygons of p sides, and let q such faces meet at each vertex. (A convenient nomenclature for the solid is $\{p, q\}$.) The internal angle of a regular polygon is equal to $(2p-4)/p$ right angles. The sum of the face angles meeting at a vertex must obviously be less than four right angles, so that

$$q\left(\frac{2p-4}{p}\right) < 4 \quad \text{or} \quad 1-\frac{2}{p} < \frac{2}{q}$$

$$\text{or} \quad \frac{1}{p}+\frac{1}{q} \quad \text{must be} \quad > \tfrac{1}{2}$$

$$\text{or} \quad (p-2)(q-2) < 4.$$

The only values of p and q (which must be integers) satisfying this inequality are

$$\{3,3\} \quad \{3,4\} \quad \{4,3\} \quad \{3,5\} \quad \text{and} \quad \{5,3\}.$$

As we shall see later, only the first three of the regular solids can occur as the shapes of crystals, but all are said‡ to have been observed as the shapes of the skeletons of certain microscopic sea animals called radiolaria (Fig. 26, Plate V).

† *Regular Polytopes*, H. S. M. Coxeter, Methuen, London (1948), p. 13.
‡ On this point see the note to Plate V.

Before we leave the regular solids we may note a relation between certain pairs which is of interest in connexion with the semi-regular solids, to which we come next. We saw in Chapter I that a circle can be drawn through the vertices of a regular polygon. If tangents are drawn to the circle through the vertices we obtain another polygon whose inscribed circle is the circumscribed circle of the first polygon. The polygons may be described

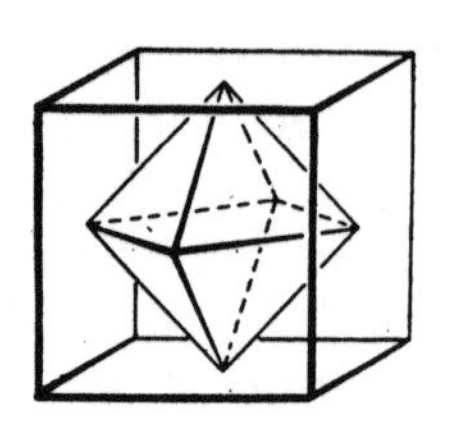
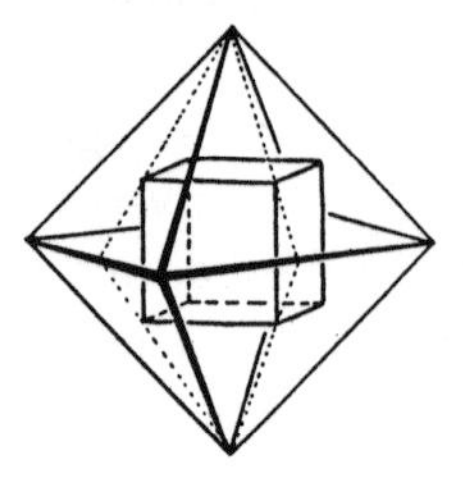

FIG. 27. Reciprocal polyhedra: cube and octahedron.

as reciprocals; they are similar in shape and have the same numbers of edges (and vertices). A property of the regular solids is that not only are their faces tangential to a sphere (inscribed or in-sphere) but also their vertices lie on a sphere (circumscribed or circum-sphere). We may expect therefore to find pairs of related polyhedra, the in-sphere of one being the circum-sphere of the other. This can be expressed by saying that the faces of one polyhedron are tangential to the circum-sphere of the other at its vertices, or that a polyhedron with f faces and c vertices becomes one with c faces and f vertices. The figures in Table 3 show that the cube is related in this way to the octahedron (Fig. 27) and the regular dodecahedron to the icosahedron. The tetrahedron is clearly reciprocal to, or the dual of, itself.

Semi-regular Solids

The regular solids have all their faces regular polygons of the same kind. If we retain the condition that all faces are regular polygons but allow regular polygons of more than one kind, we find three sets of semi-regular polyhedra which have the property that all their vertices lie on the surface of a sphere. They comprise a group of thirteen solids which are closely related to the regular solids and two families of polyhedra called regular prisms and antiprisms. These are all listed in Table 4, in which the symbols indicate the kinds and numbers of polygonal faces which meet at each vertex; for example, 3.6^2 is an abbreviation for one triangular and two hexagonal faces.

TABLE 4

The Archimedean Semi-regular Solids

	Symbol	Name	Number of Faces	Number of Vertices	Number of Edges
1	3.6^2	Truncated tetrahedron	8	12	18
2	3.8^2	Truncated cube	14	24	36
3	4.6^2	Truncated octahedron	14	24	36
4	$(3.4)^2$	Cuboctahedron	14	12	24
5	$4.6.8$	Truncated cuboctahedron	26	48	72
6	3.4^3	Rhombicuboctahedron	26	24	48
7	$3^4.4$	Snub cube	38	24	60
8	3.10^2	Truncated dodecahedron	32	60	90
9	$(3.5)^2$	Icosidodecahedron	32	30	60
10	5.6^2	Truncated icosahedron	32	60	90
11	$4.6.10$	Truncated icosidodecahedron	62	120	180
12	$3.4.5.4$	Rhombicosidodecahedron	62	60	120
13	$3^4.5$	Snub dodecahedron	92	60	150
14	$m.4^2$	Regular prisms	$n+2$	$2n$	$3n$
15	$m.3^3$	Regular antiprisms	$2n+2$	$2n$	$4n$

The first thirteen Archimedean solids are derivable by symmetrically shaving off the corners of the regular solids (a process called truncation), and this is presumably the reason why they were known so long ago. These solids, which are illustrated in Fig. 28, Plate VI, are related to some of the 3-dimensional networks described in Chapter III. The faces of these Archimedean solids are regular polygons (of more than one kind), and two, the cuboctahedron and icosidodecahedron, have the special distinction that they are the only two convex polyhedra whose faces are regular polygons of two kinds only and of which each face is entirely surrounded by faces of the other kind. Two others, the snub cube and the snub dodecahedron, have the interesting property that they cannot be brought into coincidence with their mirror images, that is, they exist in left- and right-handed forms like shoes or gloves.

Two other groups of solids whose faces *can* be regular polygons are the prisms and antiprisms, examples of which are shown in Fig. 28, Plate VI, and Fig. 29. If we take two regular polygons

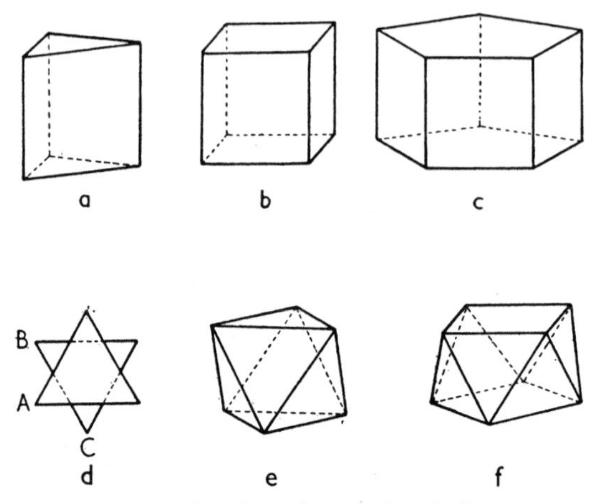

FIG. 29. Regular prisms and antiprisms.

of the same size and place one with its corners vertically above those of the other and then join the corners of the two polygons with vertical lines, we obtain a prism with sets of rectangular vertical sides. If the height of a rectangular prism is chosen to be equal to the side of the base the vertical sides become squares, and all the faces of the prism are regular polygons. Of these solids the second is the cube, but the general nomenclature is trigonal, tetragonal, pentagonal, etc., prism (Fig. 29 (a)–(c)).

Alternatively, if the upper polygon is turned into what we may call the complementary position, as in Fig. 29 (d), we can then join a corner A of the upper polygon to two corners B and C of the lower one which are at the same distance from A. The resulting solid is called an antiprism. By adjusting the height we can make each of the side faces an equilateral triangle. It will be evident that the first antiprism is an octahedron. Like the other Archimedean solids the prisms and antiprisms are isogonal, having the same number and arrangement of faces meeting at each corner, but apart from the cube and octahedron they are obviously much less symmetrical. We shall have more to say about symmetry later but we may notice, for example, that a pentagonal prism (Fig. 29 (*c*)) would present a pentagonal face to the observer only when viewed from directly above or below. It would present a quite different appearance, namely a square face, when viewed along a direction perpendicular to one of the side faces. Contrast this with the regular dodecahedron or icosidodecahedron, which present the same pentagonal appearance when viewed in any one of twelve directions. This difference between a pentagonal prism and a dodecahedron is rather like that between a cylinder (with one special axial direction) and a sphere. In fact, we could draw a cylinder inside the prism to touch all the faces, but within the regular solids we can inscribe a sphere to touch all the faces.

Corresponding to the isogonal semi-regular solids of Table 4 there are sets of isohedral bodies each of which is the reciprocal of one of the isogonal polyhedra. From this it follows that all the faces of a polyhedron of the second type are tangential to an inscribed sphere. Although all the solids of Table 4 were described by Archimedes, only one of the isohedral solids seems to have been known to the ancients. Indeed, the complete set does not appear to have been recognized until they were described by the French mathematician Catalan in 1865. We do not list the Catalan solids for they have the same numbers of edges as the corresponding Archimedean solids, and the numbers of faces and vertices are interchanged. The Catalan solids corresponding to the prisms are the bipyramids (which for $n = 4$ is the regular octahedron), and those reciprocal to the antiprisms are related to the bipyramids in the same way as the antiprisms to the prisms. Models of some of the Catalan solids are illustrated in Fig. 30, Plate VII; they are numbered to show their relation to the Archimedean solids of Fig. 28, Plate VI, and Table 4.

The one isohedral semi-regular solid known to the ancients was the rhombic dodecahedron (Fig. 30 (4)), which has long been known as the characteristic shape of crystals of the mineral garnet. This solid can be rather easily constructed from two equal cubes, one of which is cut into six square pyramids whose bases are the cube faces and their apices the central point (body-centre) of the cube. One of these six pyramids is placed on each

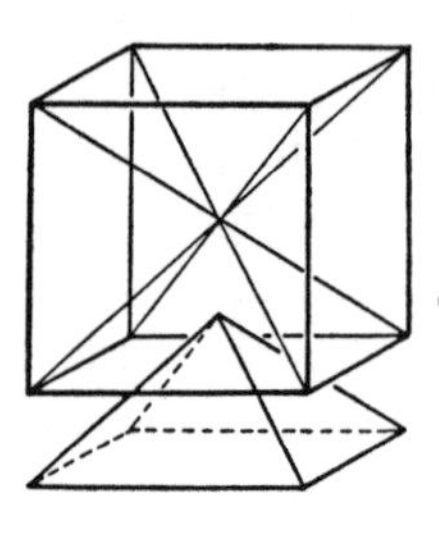

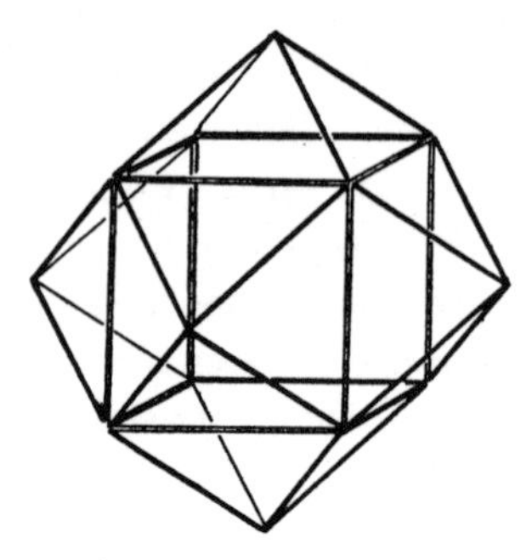

FIG. 31. Construction of rhombic dodecahedron from two cubes.

face of the other cube, as shown in Fig. 31. We shall meet the rhombic dodecahedron again in connexion with the closest packing of spheres.

On Polyhedra in general

Although, as we have seen, the Greeks had a considerable knowledge of polyhedra, it is only during the past two hundred years or so that a systematic study has been made of their properties and the relations between them. In 1758 the great mathematician Euler published his *Elementa doctrinae solidorum*, which marks the beginning of modern studies of the shapes of solids. In a polygon with C sides (or corners) the sum of the internal angles is $2C-4$, or $2(C-2)$ right angles. On a convex polyhedron having C vertices the sum of the angles of the faces is $4(C-2)$ right angles. This remarkable result, that the sum depends simply on the number of vertices, led Euler to base his classification of polyhedra primarily on corners (vertices). Thus a solid with eight vertices and seven faces was called octogonum heptaedrum. Euler was a contemporary of the Swedish botanist Linnaeus who devised a systematic classification of plants based on the numbers of stamens and pistils, and it is interesting to compare Euler's names for polyhedra with the botanical terminology of Linnaeus (e.g. hexandria trigynia).

Euler gives his name to the very simple relation

$$C+F = E+2$$

which states that the sum of the numbers of corners and faces of a polyhedron is equal to two more than the total number of edges. For example, the numbers for a cube are $8+6 = 12+2$ and for the regular dodecahedron, $20+12 = 30+2$. Euler's law can be proved in a variety of ways, of which the following is an example.

Let Fig. 16 (*a*), p. 18, represent the Schlegel diagram of a polyhedron having P_r points (vertices) in the perimeter and P_i in the interior. Then, as before, the sum of all the angles within the figure equals $180°(P_r+2P_i-2)$, whence the number of triangles is P_r+2P_i-2 and the number of faces (F) on the polyhedron is P_r+2P_i-1, since the outer polygon is one face. We may count the total number of edges in the following way. Each triangle with one side in the perimeter contributes one plus two halves, and each triangle in the interior, three halves, whence

$$E = 2P_r+\tfrac{3}{2}(2P_i-2) = 2P_r+3P_i-3.$$

The number of corners (C) $= P_r+P_i$ and therefore

$$C+F = 2P_r+3P_i-1 = E+2.$$

We may derive any desired polyhedron from one having one r-gon face and $(2P_i-2)$ triangular faces by successively removing edges like AB (when F and E each decrease by one) and/or edges like BC (involving one 3-connected vertex C) when C and F each decrease by one and E by two. (The reader may like to verify that there is no need to consider the case of an edge connecting two 3-connected vertices.) These operations are consistent with Euler's equation.

In Chapter I we saw that there are very simple relations governing the *proportions* of polygons with various numbers of sides in a plane net. For a 3-connected net

$$3p_3+4p_4+5p_5+...+p_k = 6. \qquad (a)$$

Since the faces of a convex polyhedron may be regarded as a set of polygons filling a closed surface we might expect somewhat similar relations for polyhedra. The formulae for plane nets involve *fractions* p_k of the total number of polygons because the net extends indefinitely in all directions. For polyhedra we may work with the actual *numbers* of polygons (faces), f_3 of triangles, f_4 of quadrilaterals, etc.

It is convenient to start with the general case, a polyhedron having f_k k-gon faces and c_r corners at which r edges meet. Since every edge is common to two faces and joins two corners we can count the number of edges in two ways:

$$E = \sum \tfrac{1}{2}rc_r = \sum \tfrac{1}{2}kf_k$$

and we may write

$$E = \frac{2}{m}(\sum \tfrac{1}{2}kf_k)+\left(1-\frac{2}{m}\right)\sum \tfrac{1}{2}rc_r,$$

where $2/m$ is any fraction.

Substituting in Euler's formula we have

$$F-\left[\frac{2}{m}(\sum \tfrac{1}{2}kf_k)+\left(1-\frac{2}{m}\right)\sum \tfrac{1}{2}rc_r\right]+C = 2,$$

and remembering that $F = \sum f_k$ and $C = \sum c_r$,

$$\sum (m-k)f_k+\sum [m-(\tfrac{1}{2}m-1)r]c_r = 2m. \qquad (b)$$

For $m = 4$ this becomes

$$\sum (4-k)f_k+\sum (4-r)c_r = 8, \qquad (c)$$

and for $m = 6$

$$\sum (6-k)f_k+\sum (6-2r)c_r = 12, \qquad (d)$$

The expanded form of equation (c) is

$$(f_3+c_3) = 8+0(f_4+c_4)+(f_5+c_5)+2(f_6+c_6)+.... \qquad (c')$$

This equation states that every polyhedron must possess some triangular faces and/or trihedral corners (at which three edges meet), and that these must total at least 8. For example:

	c_3	f_3
Tetrahedron . .	4	4
Cube . . .	8	0
Octahedron . .	0	8

The expanded form of equation (*d*) is

$$3f_3+2f_4+f_5 = 12+0c_3+2c_4+4c_5+...+$$
$$+0f_6+f_7+2f_8+.... \qquad (d')$$

From this equation it follows that every polyhedron must have some triangular, quadrilateral, and/or pentagonal faces, and that $3f_3+2f_4+f_5$ must be at least 12.

From these general equations we may derive relations which apply to special kinds of polyhedra. For a polyhedron having three edges meeting at each vertex (3-connected polyhedron) the equation (d') reduces to

$$3f_3+2f_4+f_5\pm 0f_6-f_7-2f_8-... = 12. \qquad (d'')$$

A special solution is

$$f_5 = 12 \quad \text{(pentagonal dodecahedron)}$$

with which we may compare the special solution of equation (*a*),

$$p_6 = 1,$$

corresponding to the plane hexagonal net. Other simple solutions are:

$$f_4 = 6 \quad \text{(cube)}$$

and

$$f_3 = 4 \quad \text{(tetrahedron).}$$

Equation (d'') shows that in addition to these solutions with only one kind of polygon there may be polyhedra with the same numbers of 3-gons, (4), 4-gons, (6), or 5-gons, (12), and in addition various numbers of 6-gons, since the coefficient of f_6 is zero,

The truncated tetrahedron and truncated octahedron are related in this way to the tetrahedron and cube:

	f_3	f_6
Tetrahedron . .	4	0
Truncated tetrahedron .	4	4

	f_4	f_6
Cube	6	0
Truncated octahedron .	6	8

The truncated icosahedron, another of the Archimedean semi-regular solids, illustrated in Fig. 28, Plate VI, is related in the same way to the regular dodecahedron, having the same number (12) of pentagonal faces and, in addition, 20 hexagonal faces. Two much simpler members of this family:

	f_5	f_6
Pentagonal dodecahedron .	12	0
Tetrakaidecahedron . .	12	2
Hexakaidecahedron . .	12	4

are illustrated in Fig. 32.

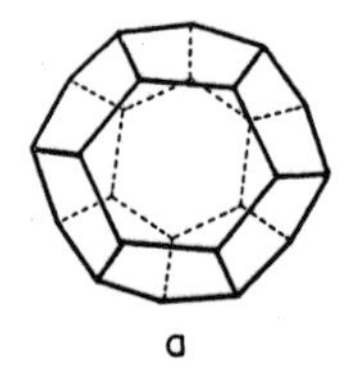

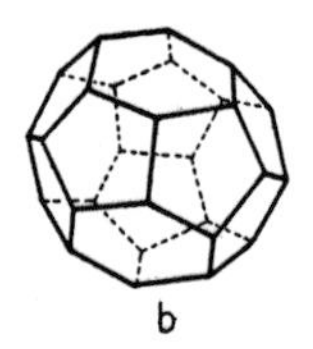

FIG. 32. (*a*) The tetrakaidecahedron: $f_5 = 12, f_6 = 2$; (*b*) the hexakaidecahedron: $f_5 = 12, f_6 = 4$.

We shall refer again to these polyhedra in connexion with polyhedral packings in Chapter III and later when we come to the structures of actual crystals. The tetrakaidecahedron may also be regarded as a member of another family of 3-connected polyhedra having 2 n-gon and $2n$ 5-gon faces:

$n = 5$: 2 5-gons and 10 5-gons (dodecahedron)

6: 2 6-gons and 12 5-gons

7: 2 7-gons and 14 5-gons, etc.

With these may be compared the (4-connected) antiprisms with 2 n-gons and $2n$ 3-gons, the first member of which is the octahedron ($n = 3$).

An interesting fact implied by equation (d'') is that there is no 3-connected polyhedron whose faces are all hexagons (whether regular or irregular). This is illustrated by the very beautiful siliceous skeletons of certain radiolaria which are like spherical baskets. The pattern of polygons of *Aulonia hexagona*, for example, is essentially hexagonal but there are some polygons with five and some with seven sides.

These equations must suffice as examples of the very simple and elegant rules governing the nature of the surfaces of convex polyhedra. We have been concerned with only two features of solids, the numbers of edges meeting at the various vertices and the kinds of faces. We shall consider later two other matters connected with polyhedra; first, the relative arrangement of faces on the polyhedron as a whole, which is a question of symmetry, and second, the packing together of polyhedra. Just as we cannot divide a plane surface into *regular* pentagons, for example, the angles being such that gaps are left, so we should expect that not all kinds of solids can be packed together without leaving holes. Various aspects of this interesting problem have been considered by a number of mathematicians, but it will be more convenient to deal with this subject at the end of the next chapter.

We should perhaps mention that we have restricted the term *regular solid* to the five convex Platonic solids. If the definition of a regular polyhedron is extended to include stellated bodies, that is, those produced by extending the faces of the Platonic solids until they meet again (preserving the rotational symmetry of the original figure), then four more solids are derived, making a total of nine regular polyhedra. (See, for example, Coxeter, op. cit., Chapter 6 and Table 1, pp. 292–3.)

CHAPTER III

REPEATING PATTERNS

One- and Two-dimensional Patterns

We are all familiar with repeating patterns, so familiar in fact that unless we are professionally interested in them we tend to take them for granted as ornaments, and seldom examine them closely. The simplest possible system would be the arrangement of equally-spaced points:

o o o o o o o o

which becomes a pattern if we place at each point some collection of points or lines, as in Fig. 33. Such patterns, linear or 1-dimensional, are used for wallpaper borders, friezes, around the edges of crockery or buildings, or anywhere, in fact, where an ornamentation is required either along an open or closed *line*.

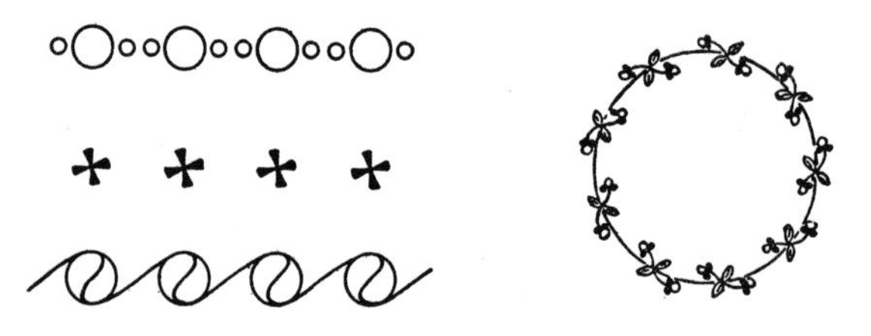

Fig. 33. Patterns repeating along an open or closed line.

If we wish to cover an *area* with a pattern we must repeat our unit of pattern along two lines inclined to one another (at any angle), that is, at the points of a mesh or net (Fig. 34 (*a*) and (*b*)). In a simple case the unit of pattern may be some discrete design (*c*) which repeats at each point of the net. Instead of focusing our attention on the points of the nets we could alternatively regard the net as consisting of a set of areas like those shaded in (*a*) or (*b*). Into the unit area we may place any desired system of points or lines. If we arrange that the pattern joins up at opposite edges as in the simple examples (*d*) and (*e*) we tend to lose sight of the quadrilateral net on which the pattern is based. This is often the intention of the designer of fabrics or wallpapers, but a careful examination of the pattern will always reveal the fundamental net on which it is based. These 2-dimensional patterns can extend indefinitely on a flat surface (or on the surface of a cylinder, which unrolls to a flat

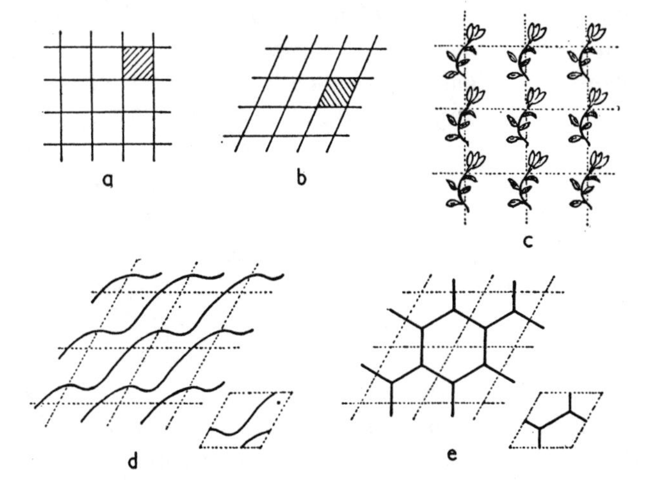

FIG. 34. Two-dimensional patterns.

surface), and for examples we have to look no further than to the wallpapers, carpets, tiled floors, and fabrics of everyday life.

Plane Nets

When listing some of the simpler 3-connected plane nets in Chapter I we gave the values of N, the number of points in the repeat unit of the pattern, and for the simplest of these nets, Net 1 of Table 1 (p. 22), the value of N is 2. Now that we have derived this net in a different way (Fig. 34 (e)) we see that each unit area contains two points. Net 3 of Table 1 and Fig. 17 is evidently formed by the repetition of a set of four points forming a square ($N = 4$), and for the configuration of Net 2 having $N = 12$ the unit area is outlined by dotted lines in Fig. 17. The value of N for any of the nets of Figs. 17 and 19 may be determined by finding the unit area and hence the number of points in the unit of pattern. It is important to check that all corners of the unit area have exactly the same environment, so that repetition of the selected area will in fact reproduce the original pattern.

Although the underlying net is a system of quadrilaterals (or in special cases, rhombuses or squares) we obtain the pattern of Fig. 34 (*e*), consisting of hexagons, by placing appropriate lines in each repeating unit. Clearly this is a way of deriving the plane nets which we discussed in Chapter I. There we were interested in the ways of dividing a plane surface into various combinations of polygons; here we have focused our attention on the basic framework on which the pattern repeats. The pattern of Fig. 34 (*e*) is one of the two ways of dividing a plane area into *similarly shaped* and *similarly oriented* polygons. The other is the basic net marked out by the dotted lines of the same diagram.

We saw in Chapter I that any system of linked points which repeats in a regular way on a plane surface has to obey certain rules and we gave equations governing the proportions of polygons of different kinds for 3-, 4-, etc., connected nets. We shall see later that in some crystals the strongest forces between the atoms link them into sheets between which relatively weak forces operate. As we might expect, these atomic patterns are like those we have been considering, as may be seen from the examples given later (see, for example, Fig. 93, p. 123, and Fig. 94, p. 127).

Patterns in Three Dimensions

We have considered patterns resulting from the repetition of some arrangement of lines or points at regular intervals along *one* line (1-dimensional pattern) and along *two* inclined lines (2-dimensional or plane pattern). The next step is to look at patterns which repeat along *three* axial directions. Such axes form a framework resembling, if the angles are right angles, the steel framework of a modern building. In the framework or lattice of Fig. 35 (*a*) we may start from any point of intersection O and arrive at neighbouring lattice points by travelling the distances a, b, or c in the directions OA, OB, or OC respectively. The repeat distances a, b, and c can have any relative values, and this is also true of the three angles AOB, BOC, and AOC. Clearly, the most symmetrical lattice is one with equal repeat distances (translations) along the three axes and all the angles right angles; in the least symmetrical, a, b, and c are all unequal in length and the angles between the axes are all unequal and different from 90°.

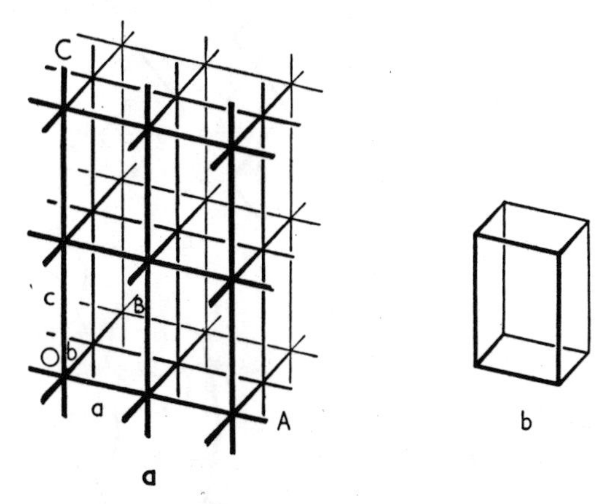

FIG. 35. A simple 3-dimensional framework.

In the plane nets of Fig. 34 the lines of the net divide the surface into what we may call *unit cells*, one of which is shaded in (a) or (b). In each unit cell we must place identical unit patterns which by repetition produce the regular 2-dimensional pattern. The analogous unit cell in the 3-dimensional net is the shape of Fig. 35 (b). If we stacked solid bodies like (b) their edges would form the lattice (a). We shall come later to the interesting question: what types of bodies can pack together *in the same orientation* to fill space?

In the unit cell of our lattice we may place any system of lines and this, by repetition in the three directions of the lattice, will give rise to a 3-dimensional pattern. A simple pattern is the actual lattice of Fig. 35 (a). If we look again at the 2-dimensional patterns of Fig. 34 we see that although they are all patterns which will cover a surface yet there are three distinct types of pattern. In (*c*) there are separate units at each point of the lattice; in (*d*) each wavy line is separate from its neighbours, whereas all the lines in (*e*) form one connected system. In 3-dimensional patterns we obviously have the same three possibilities and in addition a fourth. We may put into our unit cell patterns of four kinds (Fig. 36). When we pack together

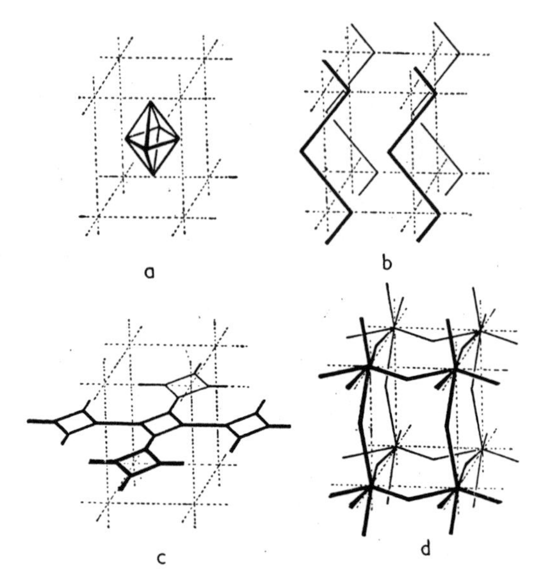

Fig. 36. Types of pattern arising from repeating units of different kinds.

unit cells of type (*a*) the units remain separate; in (*b*) the units connect up only vertically, to form continuous chains. In (*c*) they link up with units in four adjacent cells to form layers, but in (*d*) they link up to form a pattern which extends as a connected network in three dimensions. Patterns of all four kinds are found in crystals, as we shall see later in this book.

There is no limit to the number of patterns of each kind, for the unit placed in each cell may be of any degree of complexity. Just as in plane nets or polyhedra different numbers of lines (edges) may meet at different points (vertices), so this is true of 3-dimensional networks. For simplicity we shall confine our

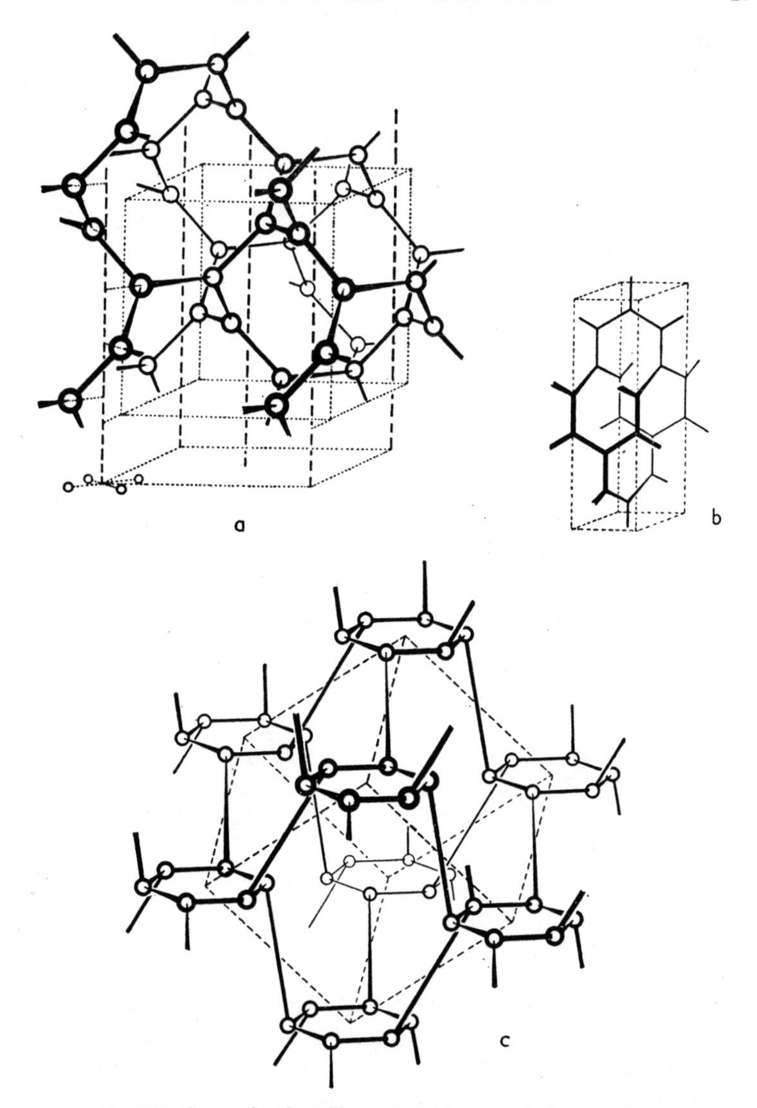

FIG. 37. Some simple 3-dimensional 3-connected networks.

attention to some of those in which the *same* number of lines meet at every point. In the case of the regular solids the maximum number of edges meeting at a corner is five; for a plane net the maximum is six if the same number of lines is to meet at each point. In 3-dimensional nets we shall find that as many as twelve lines (equal in length) can meet at every point. (This would be the case if the points were the centres of close-packed spheres—see p. 50.) Some of the simpler 3-connected nets are shown in Fig. 37, and some 4-connected nets in Fig. 38. The nets of Fig. 37 are also illustrated as stereoscopic photographs in Fig. 92, Plate XIII.

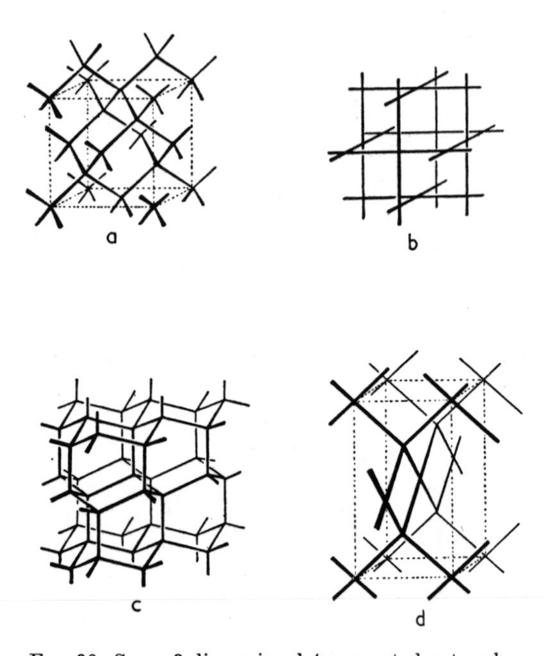

FIG. 38. Some 3-dimensional 4-connected networks.

Of the 3-dimensional nets we may distinguish some, conveniently described as *uniform nets*, which have the property that the shortest complete circuit starting out from any point along any link and returning (along another link) to the starting-point passes through the same total number (n) of points (links)

If a 3-connected net is to satisfy this condition it is only necessary that *two* n-gons meet at each point, i.e. the nets have symbols of the type $m.n^2$ like the semi-regular solids of Table 4 (p. 33). A particularly interesting net of this kind in which the shortest circuit is a 12-gon, is the net $12^2.14$, illustrated in Fig. 92, Plate XIII.

A more restrictive condition is that all *three* shortest circuits from each point should be n-gons. Three-dimensional nets of this kind, with symbols n^3, obviously form the continuation of the series starting with those regular solids which have three edges meeting at each vertex and the plane hexagonal net (6^3). The two simplest nets 10^3 are those of Fig. 37 (a) and (b), and the n^3 series is complete from $n = 3$ to $n = 10$, as set out in Table 5. Part of this series is illustrated in Fig. 91 (p. 117) in connexion with the structures of crystalline compounds of phosphorus.

TABLE 5

		n	*Symbol*
Regular solids	tetrahedron	3	3^3
	cube . .	4	4^3
	dodecahedron	5	5^3
(1-dimensional patterns .		4, 5)	..
Plane net		6	6^3
Regular 3-dimensional nets		7	7^3
		8	8^3
		9	9^3
		10	10^3

In Fig. 37 we have illustrated the nets in their most symmetrical forms, that is, with all links equal in length and with the most symmetrical arrangement of links at each point which is possible for a particular net; for (a) and (b) the angles between bonds are 120°. In such a net it is clearly possible to replace each point by an equilateral triangle, a process similar to the formation of an Archimedean solid by truncating a regular solid. Evidently the regular 3-connected nets consisting of 7-, 8-, 9-, or 10-gons become nets with triangles and 14-, 16-, 18-, or 20-gons respectively. We have then another series (Table 6), analogous to the one set out above, starting with three of the semi-regular solids (Fig. 39).

TABLE 6

		Faces or circuits	Symbol
Archimedean solids	truncated tetrahedron	3+ 6	3.6^2
	cube	8	3.8^2
	dodecahedron	10	3.10^2
	plane net	3+12	3.12^2
	3-dimensional nets	3+14	3.14^2
		16	3.16^2
		18	3.18^2
		20	3.20^2

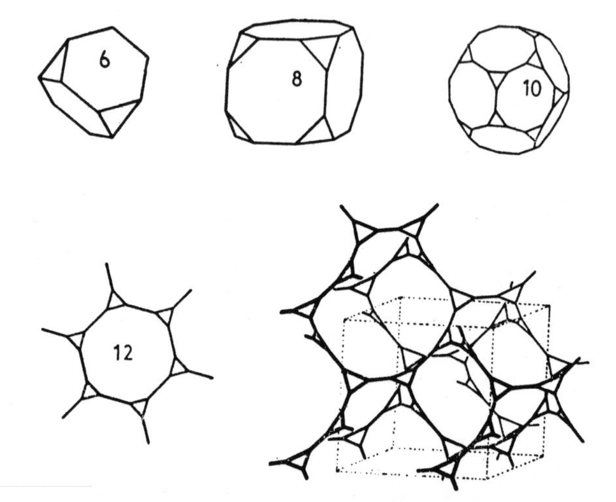

FIG. 39. Relation between semi-regular solids, plane net 3.12^2, and 3-dimensional network 3.20^2.

The Closest Packing of Spheres

At the beginning of this chapter we derived a planar net by repeating a simple system of lines in unit cells, the lines being arranged so that they joined with those in adjacent cells to form a continuous network of hexagons (Fig. 40 (*a*)). This same pattern was derived in Chapter I as one way of dividing a plane surface into polygons, where the emphasis was on the polygonal areas into which the plane was divided (Fig. 40 (*b*)). We have now derived some 3-dimensional patterns of points and lines.

There is clearly another type of 3-dimensional pattern, the packing of polyhedra to fill space, analogous to the division of a plane into polygons. We might expect the lines in our 3-dimensional nets to be the edges of polyhedra in space-filling packings of polyhedra just as the lines in the 2-dimensional net (*a*) are the edges of the polygons in (*b*). The situation is, however, not quite so simple.

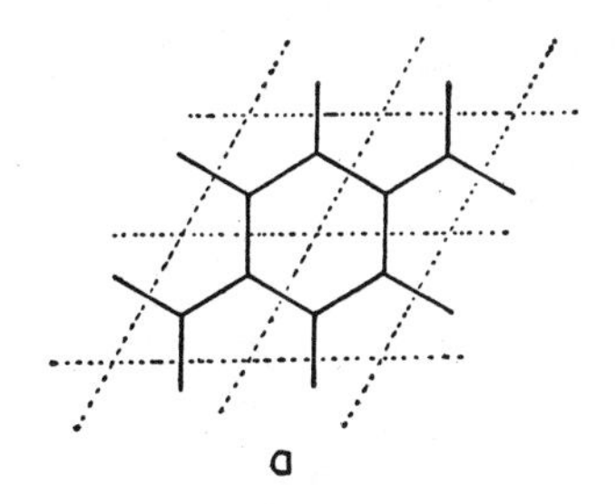

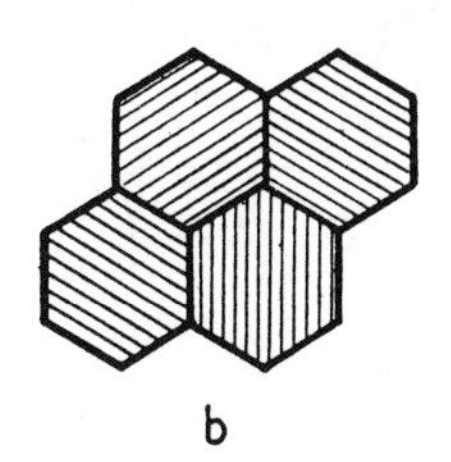

FIG. 40.

It is true that the edges of polyhedra in any packing of polyhedra do form a connected 3-dimensional net, but there are many 3-dimensional nets in which the lines do not outline convex polyhedra. In the first place, at least four edges must meet at a corner in any space-filling packing of polyhedra, and therefore there is no polyhedral packing corresponding to any 3-dimensional 3-connected net. In general, of the frameworks in which four or more lines meet at every point only a very small number correspond to polyhedral packings. For example, in the simplest 4-connected net, Fig. 38 (*a*), which represents the spatial arrangement of carbon atoms in diamond, the links do not outline polyhedra, and this is true of all the simpler 3-dimensional 4-connected nets.

We can conveniently approach the subject of polyhedral packings by considering first the closest packing of spheres. If we pack together as closely as possible a number of equal spheres resting on a plane surface we find that each is in contact with six others (Fig. 41 (*a*)). It will be noticed that this arrangement of circles in a plane is closely related to the hexagonal net

(Fig. 41 (*b*)), and if a bundle of cylindrical objects such as candles were uniformly compressed laterally the cross-section of the bundle would be this same net. The Giant's Causeway provides an example of a packing of this sort, for it consists of predominantly hexagonal columns of basalt. Equally, if we pack a number of cylindrical balloons together and then expand

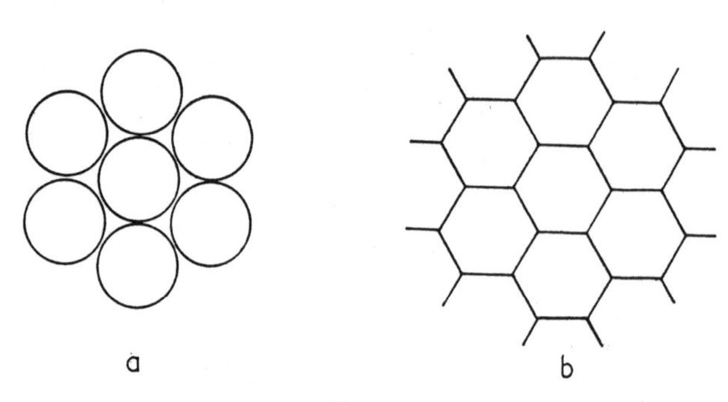

FIG. 41.

them they would tend to become hexagonal prisms. The bees' honeycomb illustrates this point most beautifully, for the plan (or cross-section) is the hexagonal net, but the honeycomb consists of a double layer of cells which are open at the ends on each side of the comb and meet in the mid-plane. Before describing this structure in more detail it is necessary to return to the closest packing of spheres.

If another similar layer of spheres is placed on top of the layer illustrated in Fig. 41 (*a*) these spheres will rest in the hollows of the first layer, so that in plan the spheres of the second layer occupy the positions shown by the dotted circles in Fig. 42 (*a*). If we wish to discuss close-packed arrangements with many layers it is convenient to show only the centres of the spheres. Those of the bottom layer may be represented by the circles (A) and those of the second layer as dotted circles (B), as in Fig. 42 (*b*). When a third layer is added there are two possible sets of positions for the centres of the spheres, either vertically above A or in the new positions C. A fourth layer could be placed with centres above A or B, and so on.

Hence there is an infinite number of ways of building a sequence of close-packed layers, the simplest being

AB, *AB*... (hexagonal closest packing)

ABC, *ABC*... (cubic closest packing)

ABAC, *ABAC*... ('double hexagonal' closest packing), etc.

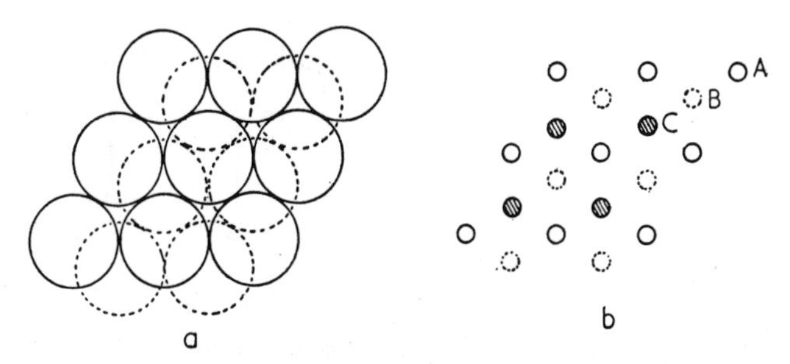

FIG. 42. The closest packing of spheres: (*a*) two adjacent layers, (*b*) positions of centres of spheres in three adjacent layers.

In all cases the spheres are equally densely packed, each having twelve equidistant neighbours, six in its own plane and three in each of the adjacent planes. Cubic closest packing takes its name from the fact that in this arrangement the spheres are at the corners and the mid-points of the faces of a cube, or more strictly, a cubic lattice. The actual closest packed layer can be seen by removing a sphere from a cube corner, as shown in Fig. 43 (*b*), Plate VIII.

Suppose that we could compress by uniform pressure on all sides a closest packed assembly of spheres made of some material such as clay which would not slide over one another. We should obtain polyhedra with twelve faces corresponding to the twelve points of contact of the spheres with their nearest neighbours. In the case of cubic closest packing each sphere would become a rhombic dodecahedron (Fig. 44 (*a*)), a shape already mentioned as the characteristic development of garnet crystals and one of the semi-regular solids of Catalan. Hexagonal closest packing gives a closely related shape (Fig. 44 (*b*)) with the same group of three faces at top and bottom as on the rhombic dodecahedron but related in this case by a plane of symmetry (see Chapter IV) because of the layer sequence *ABAB*.... We shall see shortly that there is an interesting difference if we lubricate the spheres before compressing them, so that they can slide over one another.

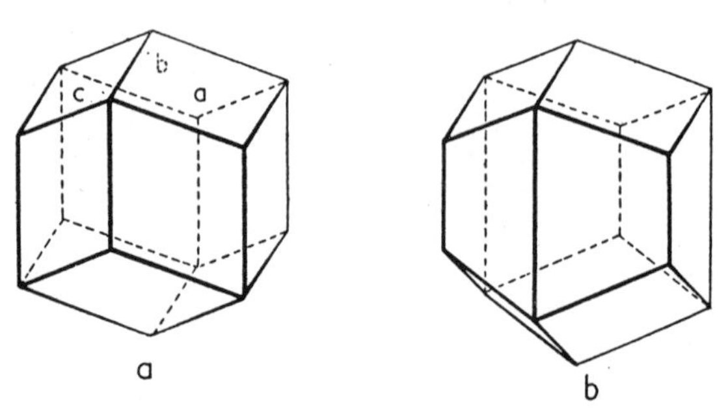

FIG. 44. Shapes resulting from uniform compression of spheres in (*a*) cubic and (*b*) hexagonal close-packing.

Suppose now that we take two bundles of candles, the ends of which have been made hemispherical, and place the bundles together end-on so that the end of each candle fits between the hemispherical ends of three candles of the other bundle, just as one sphere of a closest packed layer fits into the depression formed between three spheres of the layer below. We now press the two bundles together. Each hemispherical end becomes a 3-sided pyramid, in fact, the three faces *abc* of a rhombic dodecahedron. In the case of the honeycomb the hexagonal shape of the cells arises not from compression but from expansion, each bee striving to enlarge its own cell. The bees are working inwards from both sides of the honeycomb and probably fashion the inner ends of their cells into hemispherical cups. Whether it is pressure or surface tension acting on the soft wax which leads to the final form of the end of each cell is not certain, but it is true that the solution using the minimum quantity of wax is to form the end of each hexagonal prism into the three faces of a rhombic dodecahedron, as in the honeycomb (Fig. 45, Plate IX).

The honeycomb has attracted attention since the early days

of mathematics. Pappus of Alexandria left an account of its hexagonal plan and attributed to the bees a 'certain geometrical forethought'. In the early eighteenth century it had been proved that if we wish to terminate a hexagonal prism with three equal rhombs so that the total area shall be a minimum for a given volume these must have angles of $109\frac{1}{2}°$ and $70\frac{1}{2}°$, that is, they are the faces of a rhombic dodecahedron. The fact that these are the angles in the bees' honeycomb led the Secretary of the Royal Academy in Paris to sum up the situation (in 1739) in a famous judgement in which he denied intelligence to the bees but nevertheless found them blindly using the highest mathematics by divine guidance and command.†

The Packing of Spheres of Different Sizes

The structures of many crystals are based on the closest packing of atoms. In the simplest case, that of certain pure metals, the atoms are all of the same kind, but in many crystalline materials there are several kinds of atom of different sizes. If we refer back to Fig. 42, or preferably examine a model consisting of two or more layers of closest packed spheres, we see that there are small holes between the spheres and that these are of three kinds, as shown in Fig. 46. Even in a close-packed assembly of spheres there is room for additional small spheres, and the sizes of the spheres which exactly fit the holes of types (*a*), (*b*), and (*c*) are readily calculated. If the radius of the large closest packed spheres (X) is unity and that of the small spheres (A) is r_A, then for triangular coordination,‡ (*a*), $r_A + r_X = \frac{2}{3}(\sqrt{3})$, so that $r_A : r_X = 0{\cdot}115$; for tetrahedral coordination (*b*) this ratio is 0·225, and for octahedral coordination (*c*), 0·414. In many crystals containing atoms of more than one kind there is packing of small atoms in the interstices of a close-packed assembly of

† *On Growth and Form*, p. 530. D'Arcy W. Thompson, C.U.P., 1952.

‡ In chemistry the term *coordination compound* was introduced to describe compounds such as cobaltammines in which a number of atoms or groups are closely attached to a central metal atom forming a (finite) complex ion or neutral molecule. We shall use the word *coordination* in a more general sense and refer to the immediate neighbours of an atom or ion in a crystal as its *coordination group* and to the number of neighbours as its *coordination number*.

larger ones, and these figures give some indication of the relative sizes of atoms which can occupy the different kinds of hole.

If the radius of the smaller atom is 0·414 of the radius of the larger, as in (*c*), it is surrounded by, and in contact with, six of the close-packed atoms, and each of the latter is still in contact with twelve of its own kind. If the smaller atom is rather larger then a new arrangement of the larger atoms is adopted,

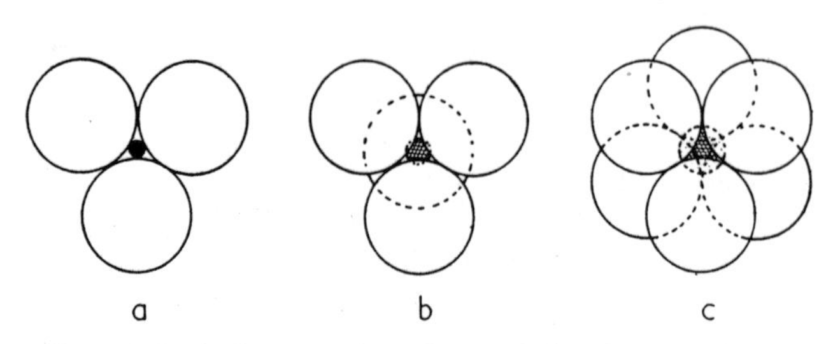

FIG. 46. Holes between three, four, and six spheres in closest packing.

in which the A atoms are surrounded by more than six X atoms. A number of important structures for crystals built of atoms of different sizes were suggested as long ago as 1883 by Barlow, who was gifted with great ability in dealing with problems of this kind. Some of the simpler arrangements found in crystals will be illustrated in Chapter V.

Ways of Packing Polyhedra to fill Space

An interesting problem, which at one time appeared to be of importance in connexion with the internal structures of crystals, concerns the packing together of identical polyhedra *in the same orientation* to fill space. Fedorov showed that there are only five kinds of polyhedra which have this property; they are illustrated in their most symmetrical forms in Fig. 47, and are the cube, hexagonal prism, rhombic dodecahedron, elongated dodecahedron, and truncated octahedron.

The fifth of the Fedorov solids arises by shaving off the corners of an octahedron until the faces have become regular hexagons. It is of special interest in another connexion. The plane net having the minimum length of line for a fixed area of repeating unit of the pattern is the regular hexagonal net, in which the smallest possible number (3) of lines meet at each point and these are arranged in the most symmetrical way possible (at 120°). The corresponding problem in three dimensions is to divide space into convex polyhedral compartments of fixed volume to give the minimum surface : volume ratio. Of the packings of convex plane-faced polyhedra (all of the

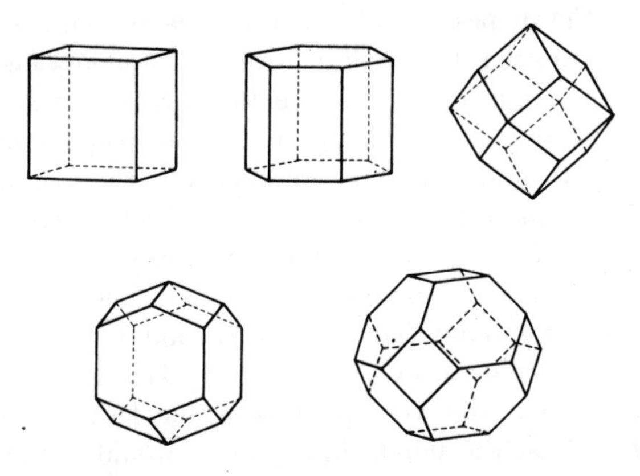

FIG. 47. The five space-filling solids of Fedorov (see also Figs. 49 and 50, Plates IX and X).

same kind) that of truncated octahedra has the smallest surface: volume ratio yet found. This packing has the minimum number (4) of edges meeting at each point and the minimum number (3) of surfaces meeting at an edge. By analogy with the planar net we might have expected the angles between the four edges meeting at any point to be $109\frac{1}{2}°$, this being the most symmetrical disposition of four lines around a point in space, and the angles between the surfaces to be 120°. These angular criteria are evidently not satisfied in the packing of plane-faced convex truncated octahedra of Fig. 50 (*c*), Plate X, for the angles between pairs of edges are 90° or 120°, the faces of the polyhedra being squares or regular hexagons. Lord Kelvin showed that a packing of tetrakaidecahedra having non-planar hexagonal faces of a particular form does indeed satisfy these criteria, and that an assembly of such solids has a smaller surface: volume ratio than that of the fifth polyhedral packing of Fedorov.

Energy has to be expended to increase the total area of interface between, for example, bubbles in a foam, and in fact this 14-faced shape does form in cases where this condition of minimum surface area is important. Examples include the grains in polycrystalline metals which have been cooled from the liquid state, and the shapes of lead shot which have been compressed sufficiently to get rid of all interstices. Pentagonal facets also occur, for the angle of a regular pentagon is 108°, very close to the tetrahedral angle. If clay pellets are wetted thoroughly so that they can glide over one another and then compressed, recognizable square and hexagonal facets develop—contrast the compression of dry pellets to rhombic dodecahedra. One investigator counted the numbers of facets on one hundred cells in elder pith and found that although the numbers ranged from 12 to 16 the average was very close to 14. The ideal case would presumably be a large volume of foam, but here the counting of the facets on the polyhedral bubbles would present more difficulty.

Stereoscopic photographs of packings of rhombic dodecahedra, elongated dodecahedra, and truncated octahedra are shown in Figs. 49 (*a*), (*b*), and 50 (*c*), Plates IX and X.

In the space-fillings of Fedorov it was a condition that all the polyhedra must be oriented similarly. If we were allowed to turn some of them round then we could admit, for example, the trigonal prism. Without this restriction the solutions are more numerous, and only certain aspects of the problem have been studied. For example, the combinations of regular and semi-regular solids (in this case, the Archimedean solids and prisms) which can pack without leaving interstices have been listed by Andreini in 1907. If we allow only one kind of solid the cube is the only one of the regular solids which satisfies this condition, and the truncated octahedron is the only one of the Archimedean solids. Neither tetrahedra nor octahedra alone fill space, but a combination in the proportion of two tetrahedra to one octahedron does do so, as might be expected from our discussion of the closest packing of spheres. The combinations, equal numbers of truncated cubes and octahedra, and equal numbers of cuboctahedra and octahedra, are easily visualized (Fig. 48), and others involving only two kinds of polyhedra are:

tetrahedra and truncated tetrahedra,
octagonal prism and truncated cuboctahedron,
octagonal prism and cube,
3-prism and 12-prism,
3-prism and 6-prism,
3-prism and 4-prism.

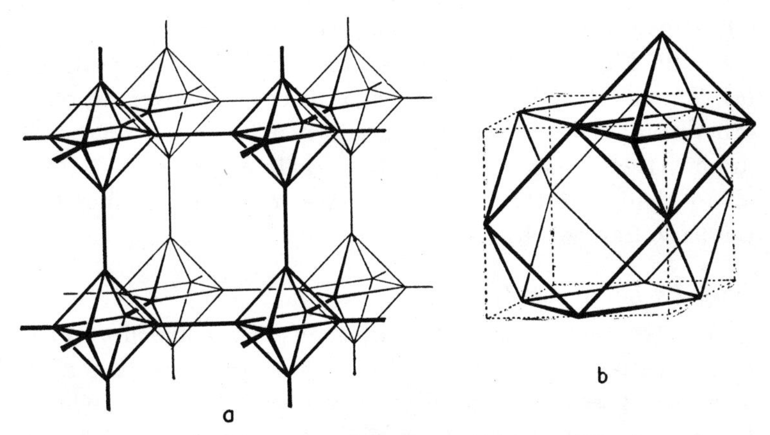

Fig. 48. Space-filling by equal numbers of (*a*) truncated cubes and octahedra, and (*b*) cuboctahedra and octahedra.

The combinations of prisms follow directly from the plane nets consisting of regular polygons which have been illustrated in Fig. 22. These plane nets can obviously represent sections through, or projections of, packings of prisms.

We shall conclude this discussion of space-filling by polyhedra by mentioning two packings of irregular polyhedra which are of interest in connexion with crystal structures. For polyhedral packings in which only four edges meet at each vertex we are restricted to those polyhedra which have only three edges meeting at a vertex. In Chapter II we noted a family of polyhedra of this kind, starting with the pentagonal dodecahedron, having twelve pentagonal faces and in addition some hexagonal faces:

a 12-hedron: $f_5 = 12$

b 14-hedron: $f_5 = 12, f_6 = 2$

c 16-hedron: $f_5 = 12, f_6 = 4.$

It is found that *a* and *b* can pack together, in the proportion of one dodecahedron to three 14-hedra to fill space, and that *a* and *c* can also fill space, in the proportion of two dodecahedra to one 16-hedron. In the latter case the pentagonal dodecahedra must be distorted slightly from the regular form so that four can meet around a point; this necessitates face angles of $109\frac{1}{2}°$ instead of 108°. These and other space-fillings are illustrated in Figs. 49 and 50, Plates IX and X. In the packings (*a*), (*b*), and (*c*) of Fig. 50 four edges meet at each vertex, or in other words the vertices and edges form a 4-connected network in which there are rather large polyhedral interstices. In Chapter VI we shall show that all three of these networks are found as the basic frameworks of certain crystals.

Open Packings of Polyhedra

We have been interested in arrangements of polyhedra which pack together, face to face, without leaving gaps. It is also, of course, possible to visualize more open packings in which, for example, only a proportion of the faces of each polyhedron are in contact with faces of other polyhedra. In others we could imagine the polyhedra touching only along edges, and in the most open arrangements possible there could be contacts only between the corners of the polyhedra. Some of the ways in which octahedra may be assembled with only a proportion of their edges and corners in contact are described in Chapter VI.

The least dense packings of polyhedra will arise if the polyhedra are in contact only at their vertices. Such arrangements can be derived from the appropriate *n*-connected frameworks by joining the mid-points of the bonds meeting at each point. For regular tetrahedra we require those 4-connected frameworks which can be constructed with equal links meeting at the tetrahedral angle ($109\frac{1}{2}°$). (Not all 4-connected networks can be constructed with a tetrahedral arrangement of links at each point; see, for example, the network of Fig. 38 (*b*).) If the mid-points of the links meeting at each point are then joined, a tetrahedron is formed around each point of the original framework, as in Fig. 51 (*a*). Some of the simplest open packings of tetrahedra are found as the atomic arrangements in crystalline silica

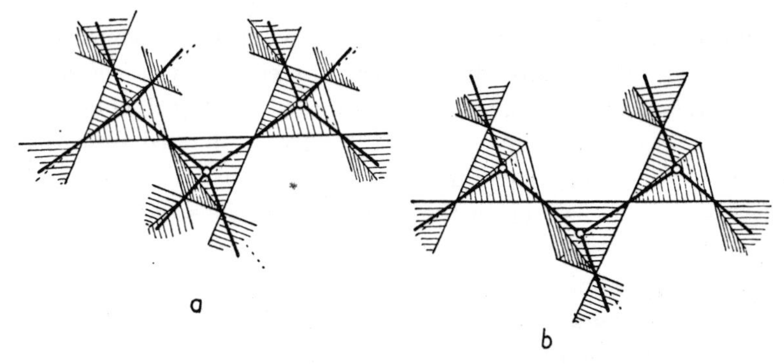

FIG. 51. Linking of polyhedra through corners.

and certain silicates, the structural unit in these crystals being a tetrahedral SiO_4 (or AlO_4) group; they are illustrated in Figs. 95 and 96, Plates XIV and XV.

Even more open packings of tetrahedra arise if only three corners are shared with other tetrahedra, as we shall find to be the case in crystalline phosphorus pentoxide, where the structural unit is the tetrahedral PO_4 group. Such packings can obviously be derived from 3-connected networks, as shown in Fig. 51 (*b*).

We see that 3-dimensional frameworks of points and lines, assemblies of polyhedra which fill space, and the open packings of polyhedra, are all interrelated, and in Chapters V and VI we hope to show that they are intimately connected with the arrangements of atoms in crystals of many kinds.

CHAPTER IV

THE SHAPE AND SYMMETRY OF CRYSTALS

Ideal and Distorted Crystals

THE logical sequel to our discussion of polyhedra is some consideration of the shapes of crystals. The earth's crust contains a great variety of materials of different chemical compositions, and in the course of time these have solidified from the molten state or separated from solution. Beautiful examples of crystals are to be seen in the mineral collections in museums; some natural crystals of quartz are illustrated in Fig. 5 (*a*) Plate 1. Crystals may readily be grown of substances such as ordinary (potassium) alum, sodium chlorate,† hypo (sodium thiosulphate), or Epsom salts. If a warm saturated solution is left to cool slowly small 'seed' crystals will be obtained which may then be suspended on small loops at the ends of lengths of fine wire in a solution saturated at room temperature. This solution is then left to evaporate. In this way large octahedral crystals of alum can be grown. A pure solution of sodium chlorate yields crystals of cubic shape, but the addition of hypo to the solution encourages the development of additional (tetrahedron) faces. If there is sufficient hypo in the solution the crystals grow as simple tetrahedra, but with intermediate concentrations the crystals develop very elegant combinations of faces of both cube and tetrahedron. Some crystals of alum and sodium chlorate grown in this way in the laboratory are illustrated in Fig. 5 (*b*), Plate 1.

The characteristic shapes of the crystals of some common substances and of the mineral garnet are shown in Fig. 52. It will be noticed that those of salt and alum are two of the five regular solids, the cube and octahedron respectively, that garnet

† It should be noted that organic materials such as filter-paper or rag which have been soaked in sodium chlorate solution and then allowed to dry are dangerously inflammable.

crystallizes with a shape which we met as one of Fedorov's five space-filling solids, and that in these three drawings all the faces of a crystal are identical in shape and size. The other two crystals illustrated are less 'regular' in shape. In this chapter we shall have to define more carefully what we mean by such terms as 'regular' and 'symmetrical'.

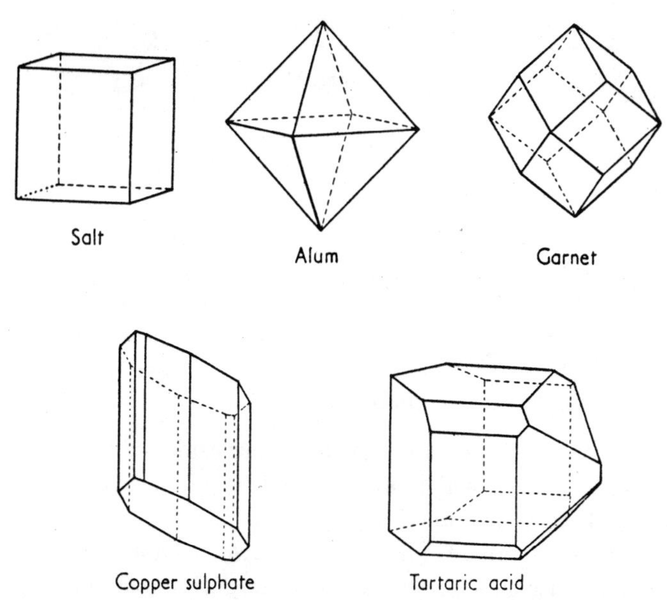

FIG. 52. Crystals of some common substances.

When describing a crystal of alum as an octahedron we were careful to specify that the crystal must be suspended in the solution and grown slowly. Crystals are not, however, usually grown under such ideal conditions. If, for example, a crystal grows on the bottom of a vessel, resting all the time on one face, it cannot grow equally in all directions. It is now supplied with material on all sides except its base, and naturally its shape will be a distorted version of the ideal shape. Roughly, we might expect a half-crystal (Fig. 53 (*a*)), the lower half of the cube being missing because deposition of material was not possible on the lower (shaded) face. The crystal is still a rectangular block and not very different in appearance from the complete cube. In the case of a tetrahedron resting on one face the shape is not affected, because a tetrahedron retains the same shape if a piece is sliced off parallel to one face (Fig. 53 (*b*)). In the case of an octahedron lying on one face, however, the effect on its appearance is more drastic (Fig. 53 (*c*)). If now, in addition, the crystal is growing near to others so that other faces are starved of

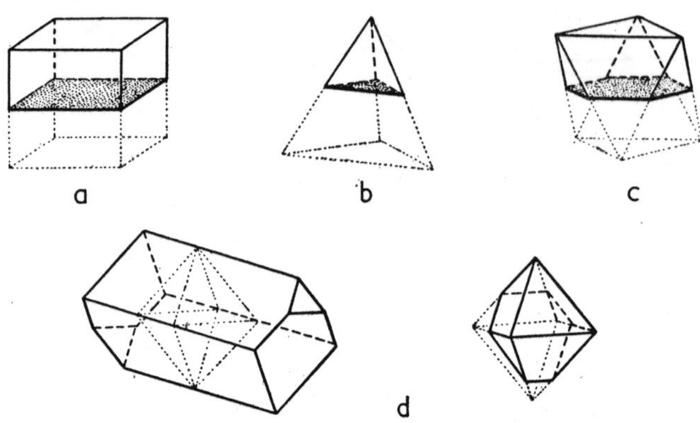

FIG. 53. Effect of growth conditions on the shapes of crystals.

material, then we get shapes even further removed from regular octahedra, crystals which might not at first sight even be recognized as distorted octahedra (Fig. 53 (*d*)).

Very few crystals of minerals have grown under ideal conditions; generally they grew close together, often starting to grow on the surfaces of other crystals which had deposited earlier. For this reason the crystals of a particular mineral usually present very different appearances, even though they may all be distorted versions of the same 'ideal' shape. This was the peculiar difficulty which confronted the early crystallographers. The crystals of a mineral such as quartz appeared to have so many different shapes, often no two alike in a large number of specimens, that there seemed to be no laws governing their shapes. If this were the case there could hardly be a science of crystallography.

The Early Crystallographers

The first great advance was made in 1669 by Nicolaus Steno. This versatile gentleman was born in Copenhagen in 1638, the son of a goldsmith. He first studied anatomy and physiology, and we find him at Florence in the position of physician-in-ordinary to the Grand Duke Ferdinand II. It was during this period at Florence that he became interested in geology and published (in Latin) his work on the angles between the faces of quartz crystals. (Later he returned to his native city as Professor of Anatomy (1672); he died at Schwerin in 1686.)

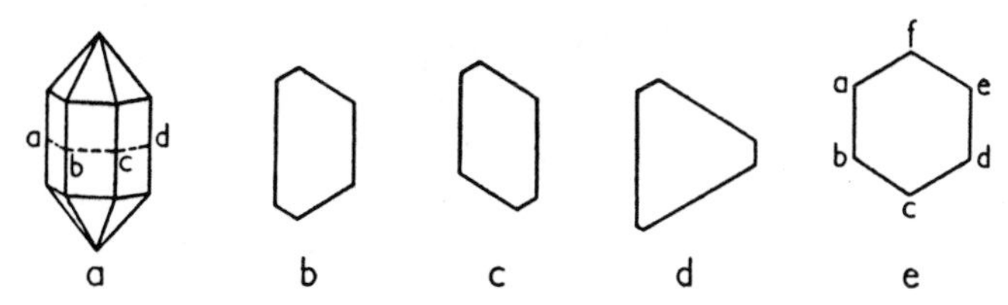

FIG. 54. Quartz crystal and sections of distorted and ideal crystals.

Steno made a detailed study of quartz crystals, the ideal shape of which is shown in Fig. 54 (*a*) and (*e*). He cut sections of various distorted crystals and traced their outlines on paper. Then by measuring the angles he found that corresponding angles of different sections were always the same, regardless of the actual sizes and shapes of the sections. The importance of this work lay in the fact that it showed that the shapes of all quartz crystals, however much distorted from the ideal, could result from the same fundamental mode of growth. If the crystal had been lying on one face it would be flattened as in Fig. 54 (*b*). If it had grown near other crystals so that the growth on certain faces was retarded owing to shortage of material in the solution, then different types of distortion resulted (Fig. 54 (*c*) and (*d*)). In all cases, however, the faces remained plane and always inclined at the same angles one to another.

Steno's work was extended and generalized by Domenico Guglielmini, who was born in 1655 in Bologna and died in Padua in 1710. Guglielmini appears to have been equally versatile. His early work was concerned with hydraulic engineering, after which he turned to a study of crystals, becoming Professor of Mathematics first at Bologna and then at Padua. Further study of this fundamental question of the constancy of the angles between crystal faces was made by a Frenchman, Jean Baptiste Louis Romé de l'Isle (1736–90). De l'Isle first followed a military career in the East, from which he returned to Paris in 1764 and eked out his pension by giving private lessons in mineralogy. He made very extensive measurements on crystals, and his first important crystallographic publication, *Essai de Cristallographie*, appeared in 1772.

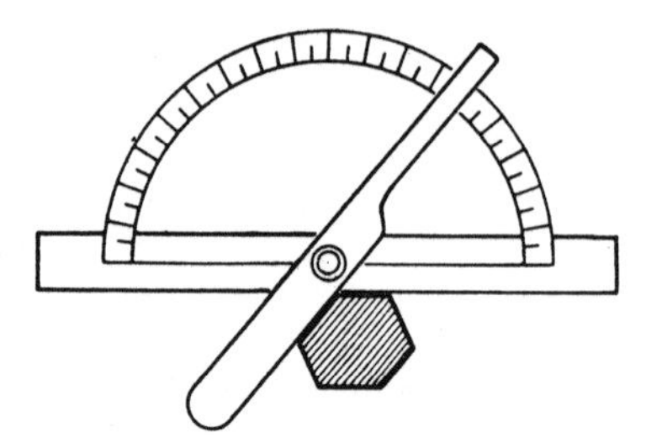

FIG. 55. Contact goniometer.

At first de l'Isle was, like Steno, limited to measuring angles on outlines of crystal sections drawn on paper, but during the course of his work his assistant Carangeot invented (in 1780) the earliest type of crystal-measuring instrument, the contact goniometer (Fig. 55). While this instrument was a great advance on the paper tracings of Steno it could only be used on large crystals, and even so its accuracy was not very high. A much more accurate way of measuring the angles between crystal faces depends on using them as little mirrors to reflect a beam of light. A beam of light from a fixed source passes through a slit system and is reflected from one face of the crystal, the reflected beam being observed in a (fixed) telescope (Fig. 56). The crystal is then rotated until the beam reflected from the next face is observed through the telescope. The angle through which the crystal was turned is the angle between the normals to the faces, since when any face is in the reflecting position its normal must lie in the direction of I. In this way the interfacial angles can be measured very precisely, in fact much more precisely than the planarity of actual crystal faces justifies. Such an instrument is called a reflecting goniometer.

The first instrument of this kind was described by Wollaston in 1809. William Hyde Wollaston (1766–1828) was born in Chislehurst, Kent. He went to Cambridge and took up medical practice, but gave this up in 1801 to devote himself to chemistry. Versatility seems to have been a characteristic of many scientists of these days and Wollaston was no exception, for he made

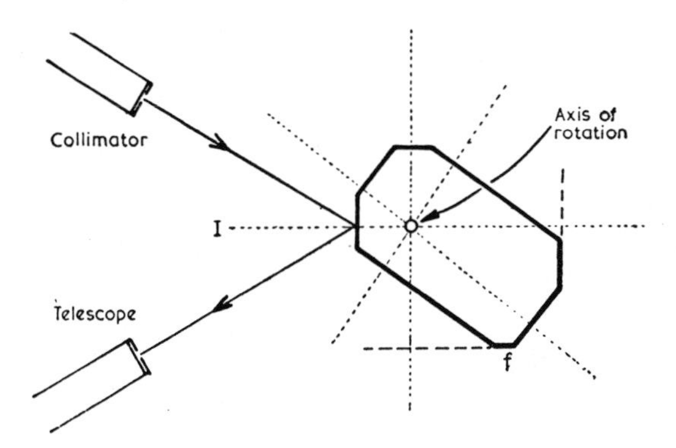

FIG. 56. Principle of the reflecting goniometer.

original discoveries in chemistry, pathology, crystallography, physics, astronomy, and botany. He is perhaps more generally known as the inventor of the camera lucida and the reflecting goniometer, and as the discoverer of two of the less common chemical elements, palladium and rhodium.

The Stereographic Projection

The introduction of the goniometer was an event of outstanding importance in the development of crystallography, for it was now possible to find the angular relationships between all the faces on a crystal. This led naturally to the classification of the types of symmetry exhibited by crystals, a subject we deal with in the next section. We said that the reflecting goniometer measures the angles between face-normals. This suggests a way of representing a crystal by a set of lines perpendicular to its faces instead of a perspective drawing.

If we imagine the crystal placed at the centre of a sphere and the face-normals extended to meet the surface of the sphere, we have on the latter a set of points representing the faces of the crystal (Fig. 57 (*a*)). Some of the points may lie on the equator, others in the northern or southern hemispheres. If now we join all the points in the northern hemisphere to the South Pole and mark on the equatorial plane *ABCD* the points (•) where these connecting lines intersect, we have within a

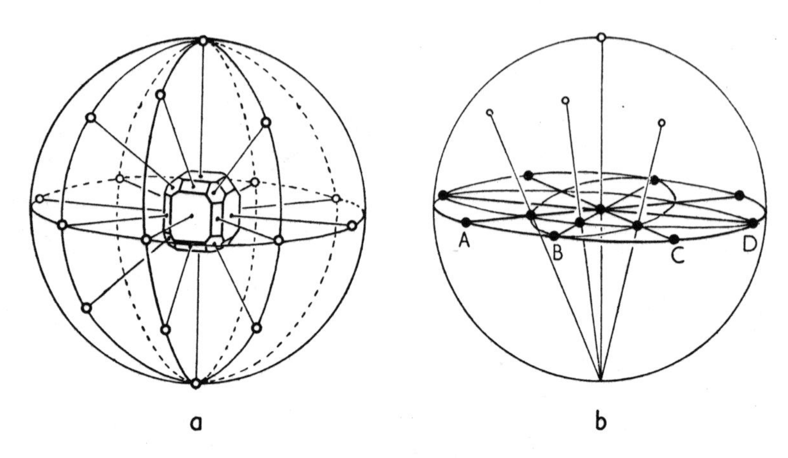

Fig. 57. Stereographic projection.

single circle a representation of the faces on the upper half of the crystal. By connecting points in the southern hemisphere to the North Pole and marking the points where these connecting lines pass through the equatorial plane as small open circles (○), we can represent the whole of the crystal within the circle *ABCD*. (For examples see Fig. 58.)

This *stereographic projection* was in fact introduced (by Neumann in 1823) only fourteen years after the invention of the reflecting goniometer. Not only does it provide a very neat representation of a crystal, but it also has the important property that since we are dealing with face-normals we are not concerned with the relative sizes of faces. In other words, all crystals of a given sort, whether perfectly developed or distorted, will have the same stereographic projection, provided there is at least a trace of each face.

Stereographic projections of some simple shapes are shown in Fig. 58.

The reader may notice that in the case of a distorted crystal our simple way of deriving the stereographic projection of a crystal is not entirely satisfactory, for it may be impossible to find a point within the crystal such that the normals from the

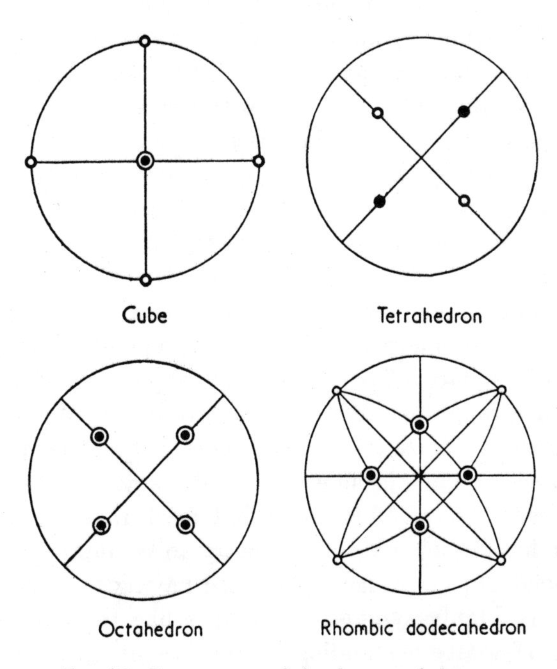

FIG. 58. Stereograms of simple crystal shapes.

point to the faces all pass through the corresponding faces (Fig. 56). This, however, is irrelevant, for the goniometer measures, and the stereographic projection represents, the angles between face-normals regardless of the relative sizes of the faces. If by chance a particular face on a large distorted crystal is so small that when it is rotated about a particular axis it does not intercept the beam of light from the collimator (as, for example, the face *f* in Fig. 56) the crystal can always be translated on one of two slides in order to bring any face into the light beam.

The Symmetry of Crystals

Crystals owe their beauty not only to their colours and transparency but also to their shapes, to the fact that facets are repeated around the crystal with a certain regularity. We have described the early attempts to measure the angles between crystal faces because a proper understanding of the symmetry of crystals was not possible until the relations between the faces were known. Once we know the angles between all the pairs of faces on a crystal we can see how the faces are related to one another. Symmetry is concerned with the relations between the various parts of a body. If there is a particular relation between these parts then we say that the object possesses certain *elements of symmetry.*

The simplest elements of symmetry are (*a*) axis of symmetry, (*b*) centre of symmetry, and (*c*) plane of symmetry. An equilateral triangle presents the same appearance after turning through a third of a revolution (in its own plane). Similarly the corners of a square fall over their original positions if the square is turned through one quarter of a revolution. We have been rotating these figures about lines (axes) perpendicular to their planes and passing through their mid-points. These axes are called, respectively, 3-fold and 4-fold axes. Likewise, a regular hexagon has a 6-fold axis of symmetry and a dumb-bell a 2-fold axis. Solid objects range from those having no symmetry at all to very highly symmetrical shapes like the cube or octahedron. If a cube is standing on one face, it is evident that it has 4-fold axes emerging from the mid-points of the faces. If balanced on an edge it will present the same appearance after rotation through a half-turn, that is, the lines joining the mid-points of opposite edges are 2-fold axes of symmetry, and if balanced on a corner and viewed from above the 3-fold symmetry is obvious (Fig. 59). Since all the six faces of a cube are similar and the eight corners and twelve edges are equivalent, the cube has a rather large number of axes of symmetry, in fact, three 4-fold, four 3-fold, and six 2-fold axes. It will also be noticed that a cube is symmetrical about its mid-point (body-centre), that is, if we start from any point on the surface and travel along a line passing through the centre of the cube to a point the same distance the other side of the centre then this point is similar in every way to that from which we set out. The cube is said to be centro-symmetrical. A triangle or tetrahedron does not possess this type of symmetry.

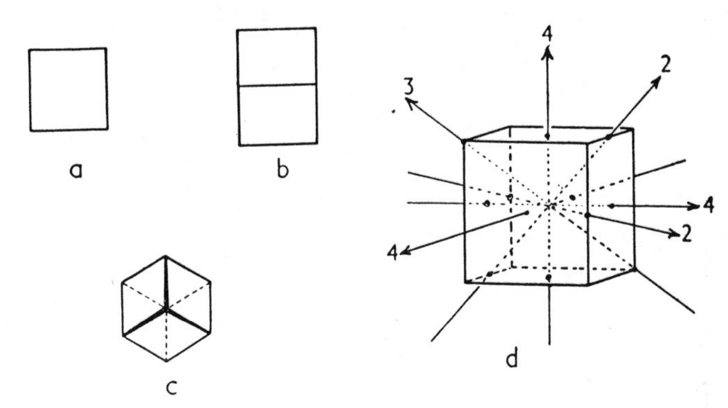

FIG. 59. Symmetry of the cube.

The other type of symmetry element we mentioned was the plane of symmetry. Many familiar objects have no axes or centre of symmetry but quite clearly have symmetry of another kind. Whereas a square table has a 4-fold axis and a rectangular table a 2-fold axis of symmetry (perpendicular to the floor and passing through the middle of the table top) a chair is symmetrical in another way. We could say that it was the same at the right and left sides, or if we imagined the chair to be cut in two (vertically) and one half placed against a mirror, we should find that the reflection in the mirror reproduced the other half of the chair. We say that the chair has a plane of symmetry. Many common objects have one plane of symmetry and no other symmetry, for example, a pair of semi-detached houses or a mantelpiece. The reader may like to satisfy himself that a cube has no fewer than nine planes of symmetry.

There is one other kind of symmetry element possessed by some crystals which we must mention here, the axis of rotatory inversion. An axis of 4-fold rotatory inversion, written $\bar{4}$, combines the process of rotation through 360°/4 with *simultaneous* inversion through a centre of symmetry, so that a face A of a tetrahedron is turned successively into B, then C, then D (Fig. 60 (a)). The operation of this type of axis is most easily shown in a stereographic projection (Fig. 60 (b)). Rotating A clockwise through 90° and then inverting brings it to D. We must emphasize that $\bar{4}$ is not equivalent to a 4-fold axis plus a centre

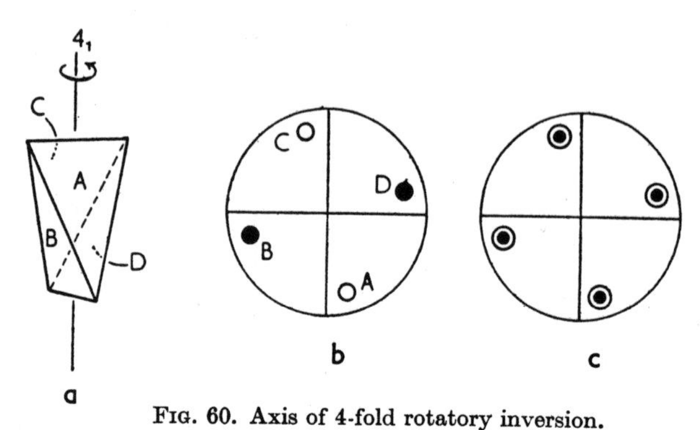

FIG. 60. Axis of 4-fold rotatory inversion.

of symmetry, for this combination would produce a set of eight faces arranged as shown in Fig. 60 (c). It can easily be verified that $\bar{1}$ is a centre of symmetry, $\bar{2}$ is equivalent to a plane of symmetry (also written m), $\bar{3}$ to an ordinary 3-fold axis plus a centre of symmetry, and $\bar{6}$ to a 3-fold axis plus a plane of symmetry perpendicular to it (Fig. 61).

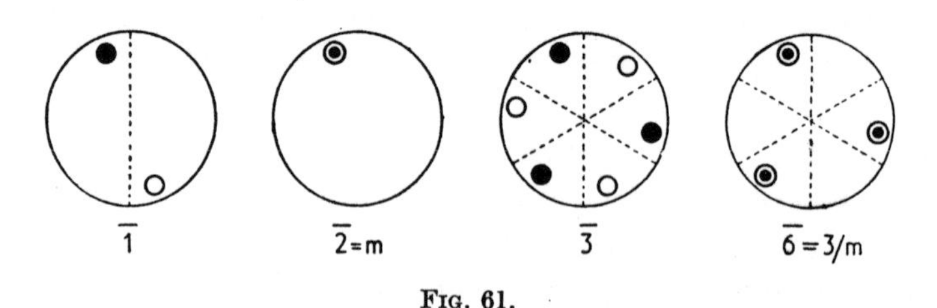

FIG. 61.

It is found as a matter of observation that the only symmetry elements exhibited by crystals are the axes 2, 3, 4, and 6, and the axes of rotatory inversion $\bar{1}$, $\bar{2}$, and $\bar{4}$. Some crystals have no symmetry at all, others only a centre, others only a plane, while some have very much higher symmetry, the most symmetrical having all the symmetry of the cube itself. As early as 1830 it was established that there are thirty-two classes of symmetry (*point-groups*), that is, symmetry elements or combinations of symmetry elements, exhibited by crystals. They are grouped into seven *crystal systems*. Some examples of crystals exhibiting different types of symmetry are shown in Fig. 62.

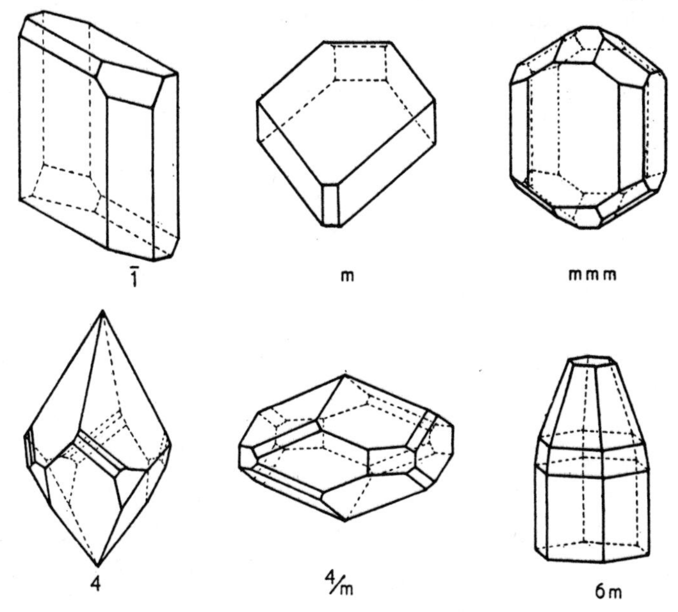

FIG. 62. Crystals illustrating different types of symmetry.

A point of some interest is the occurrence of only 2-fold, 3-fold, 4-fold, and 6-fold symmetry in crystals; this point will be considered shortly when we come to the internal structure of crystals.

Early Ideas on the Structure of Crystals

The regular shapes of crystals must have invited speculation about their internal structures long before the first scientific studies mentioned earlier in this chapter were made. Without delving too deeply into history we may note that Hooke, a contemporary of Sir Isaac Newton, observed that by piling up musket shot in a regular way he could imitate the shapes of crystals of alum. Fig. 43, Plate VIII, shows that by removing spheres from the corners of a set of cubic close-packed spheres we expose a surface corresponding to an octahedral facet on a cube. This we now know to be an accurate picture (on a large scale) of the structure of a metal such as copper, in which the atoms are in fact arranged in cubic close-packing, but we must remember that the atomic theory of Dalton was not set out until 1808.

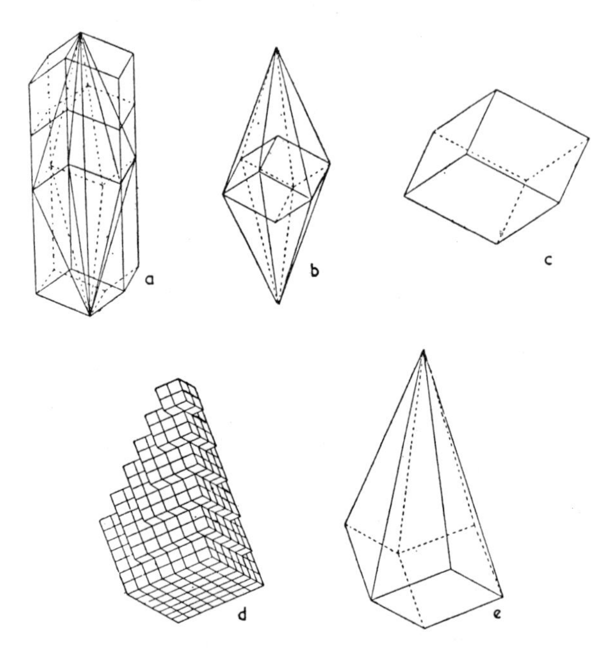

FIG. 63. (*a*) and (*b*) crystals of calcite (after Bergman), (*c*) cleavage rhomb, (*d*) stacking of cleavage rhombs to produce the shape of a crystal (*e*) of 'dog-tooth' spar (after Haüy).

The first real progress towards a knowledge of the internal structure of crystals came from considering, not the packing of spheres but the packing of polyhedra. Calcite or Iceland spar, a widely distributed mineral, is a crystalline form of calcium carbonate which forms beautiful crystals with a number of distinctive shapes, in particular, hexagonal prisms and the scalenohedral crystals known as dog-tooth spar (Fig. 63). The optical properties of Iceland spar attracted the attention of

Erasmus Bartholinus in 1670, exactly at the time Steno was studying the constancy of the angles of quartz crystals. The double refraction of this mineral was also studied by Newton and Huygens during the latter half of the seventeenth century. Another property of calcite noted by Erasmus Bartholinus and the one which is of interest here is its *cleavage*, the property of breaking along certain well-defined planes when a crystal is struck with a hammer or pressed with a knife or sharp point. One of the most perfect examples of cleavage is mica, which can be cleaved into sheets of almost any desired thinness. Diamonds cleave along octahedral planes, a fact utilized by the diamond cutter to reduce a crystal rapidly to the approximate shape and size required.

Cleavage must have been observed at a very early date. Huygens had recorded in his *Treatise on Optics* (1690) that calcite cleaves into rhombs, and moreover he measured the angles between the faces of a cleavage rhombohedron. He pictured the crystal as composed of flattened spheroids rather than spheres to account for the rhombohedral cleavage. It was found that calcite crystals of quite different shapes could be cleaved into rhombs of the type shown in Fig. 63 (*c*), and (*a*) and (*b*) are in fact copied from drawings made by Bergman in 1773. This property was given a new significance by the Abbé Haüy of Paris. Noticing that the cleavage rhombs from calcite crystals of all shapes had the same interfacial angles, Haüy suggested that all crystals of calcite could be imagined to be built of these fundamental cleavage rhombs. This is shown for a crystal of 'dog-tooth' spar in Fig. 63 (*d*), which is copied from his *Traité de Minéralogie*, published in 1801. If the elementary rhombs are sufficiently small the faces of the crystal would present the appearance of optically flat surfaces.

The importance of this idea lay in the fact that it suggested a mechanism for the formation of secondary faces on crystals (e.g. octahedral faces on the corners of a cube) and it required certain precise geometrical relations between faces of different kinds. This can be shown very simply by a 2-dimensional analogy. From the units of Fig. 64 we can build a straight edge

AB (representing a cube face) or an inclined edge AC (representing, for example, an octahedron face). There could also be edges inclined at other angles, as in the case of DE. If the dimensions of the units are a and b, then $\tan\theta_1 = b/a$, $\tan\theta_2 = b/2a$, and in general $\tan\theta$ must be equal to mb/na, where m and n are *rational integers*. Extending this concept to

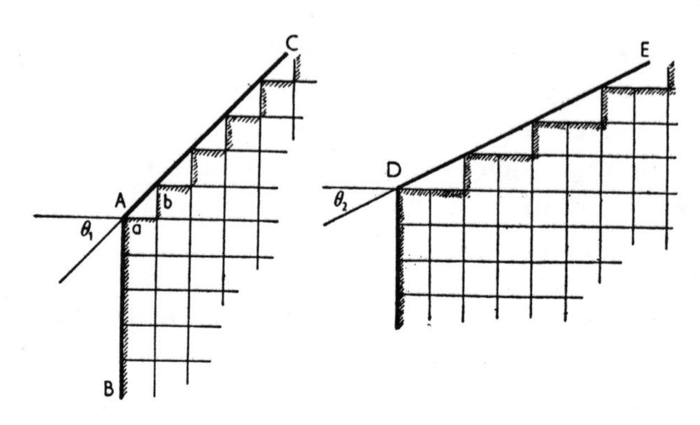

FIG. 64.

a crystal we are led to a 'law of rational intercepts'. If a reference face makes intercepts a, b, and c on three axes, then the intercepts made by any other face must be in the proportion of rational multiples of these intercepts.

In practice we do not now describe crystal faces in terms of the multiples of the standard intercepts but instead we use the reciprocals of these numbers, and this fundamental law of crystallography becomes the *Law of Rational Indices*. Three lines (not in the same plane) are adopted as axes (Fig. 65); these are often, but not necessarily, directions of edges of the crystal. A reference face ABC makes intercepts a, b, and c on these axes. The plane of any other face of the crystal, e.g. CDE, can then be defined by intercepts a/h, b/k, and c/l, where h, k, and l, the Miller indices of the face, are simple rational numbers or zero. If a face is parallel to one axis the intercept is infinite and its indices are of the type h, k, 0. Evidently, if we adopt the obvious orthogonal axes, the indices of the faces of a cube are (100), (010), and (001), and those of the rhombic dodecahedron and octahedron are of the type (110) and (111) respectively. In Fig. 65 the indices of the face *CDE* are (231).

Now although most crystals exhibit cleavage, usually much less perfect along some planes than others, the cleavages do not generally lead to a cleavage figure which by repetition can fill space. For example, fluorspar cleaves along octahedral planes

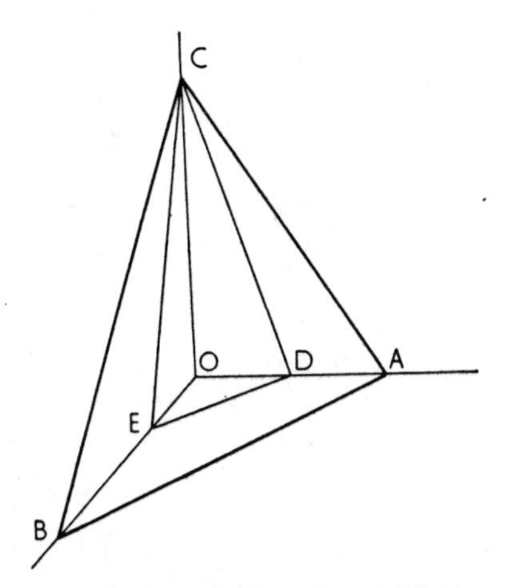

FIG. 65. The indexing of crystal faces.

to yield octahedra, but the shape of the original cube of fluorspar cannot be built from cleavage octahedra in the way that the calcite crystals can be reconstructed from cleavage rhombs because, as we have seen, the octahedron is not one of the limited number of space-filling polyhedra. The simple cleavage theory of Haüy could not therefore develop into a general theory of the structures of crystals.

The natural alternative is to focus attention on the centres of the objects which are stacked together and to find the arrangements of points in space which are consistent with the observed properties of crystals. It appeared reasonable to suppose that these basic frameworks would have the following properties: along any line drawn through two points of the framework there will be series of points with the same separations as the original pair of points, and there will be exactly the same pattern of points along any parallel line drawn through any other point of the system. Such a structure is, like a crystal, homogeneous, and consists of planes of regularly arranged points which, like the faces of crystals, obey the Law of Rational Indices.

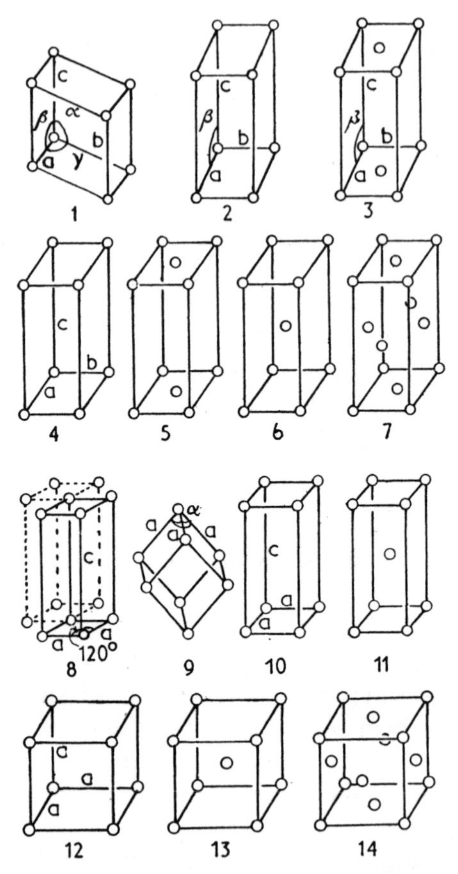

Fig. 66. The fourteen Bravais lattices.

A framework with these properties is called a *space-lattice*, and during the years 1835–48 Frankenheim and Bravais independently derived the fourteen space-lattices (Bravais lattices). Each of these lattices has the symmetry of one of the seven crystal systems; they are illustrated in Fig. 66. We do not propose to go much further into the geometrical theory underlying the structures of crystals, but it may be of interest if we indicate briefly the nature of the next step which had to be made after the nature and the number of the fundamental frameworks (lattices) had been established.

The Symmetry of Planar Arrangements of Points

In Chapter I we gave examples of the ways in which a plane surface can be divided into polygons, and at the beginning of Chapter III we saw that any repeating pattern can be referred to a basic framework or net. We did not, however, inquire how many such frameworks there are, or indeed whether their number is limited. Nor did we consider the symmetry of plane patterns. Similarly we have described 3-dimensional networks as systems of polygons rather than as structures having certain symmetries. We have done this because, as we shall show later, the same basic framework may occur in different crystals, distorted in different ways from its most symmetrical form. However, in the development of the theory of crystal structure, and what is more important, in the actual determination of the structures of crystals, symmetry is of the greatest importance. Although from the chemical standpoint we are not so much interested in symmetry as in the way in which the atoms are linked together, this little introduction to structural chemistry would hardly be complete without some discussion of a subject which is in any case of interest in itself.

There are five systems of axes for 2-dimensional patterns, or alternatively five 2-dimensional lattices with different symmetries; they are illustrated in Fig. 67. It will be seen that these lattices have 2-fold, 4-fold, and 6-fold symmetry axes, the latter implying also 3-fold axes. That these are the only types of symmetry axis which a plane repeating pattern can possess can be shown in the following way. In Fig. 68 let there be an axis of p-fold rotation perpendicular to the plane of the paper at P, and at Q one of the nearest other axes of p-fold rotation. The rotation through $2\pi/p$ about Q transforms P into P' and the same kind of rotation about P' transforms Q into Q'. It may happen that P and Q' coincide, in which case $p = 6$. In all other cases PQ' must be greater than, or equal to, PQ (since Q was chosen as one of the nearest axes), i.e. $p \leqslant 4$. The permissible values of p are therefore 1, 2, 3, 4, and 6. Since a 3-dimensional lattice may be regarded as built of plane nets the

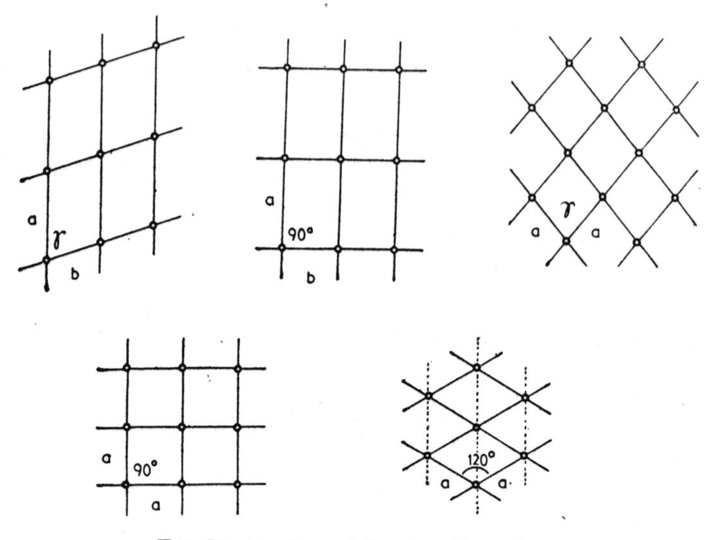

FIG. 67. The five axial systems in a plane.

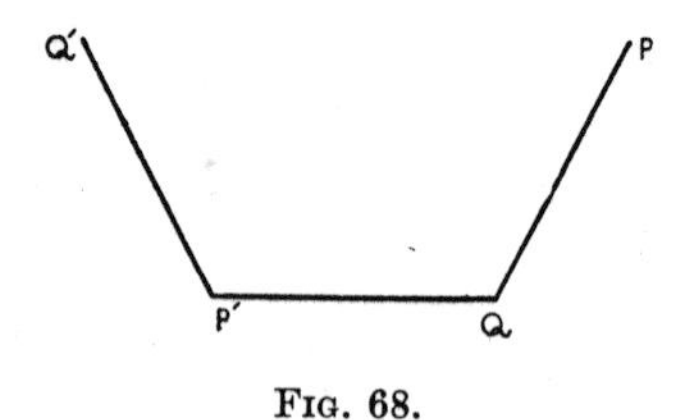

FIG. 68.

same restriction on kinds of symmetry applies to the 3-dimensional lattices, and hence to the symmetry of crystals.

Now in order to find which sorts of patterns of points are possible in 2-dimensional patterns we must know what types of symmetry elements are available. Clearly we can have points in a plane related by rotation axes (2-, 3-, 4-, or 6-fold) and by mirror-reflection lines, which are the planar equivalents of mirror planes for solid objects. There is also, however, a new type of symmetry element possible, which in one operation combines a reflection across a line with a translation of one-half the distance between lattice points (*glide reflection line*). The translation of one-half is necessary in order to bring the point back into coincidence with the next lattice point (Fig. 69).

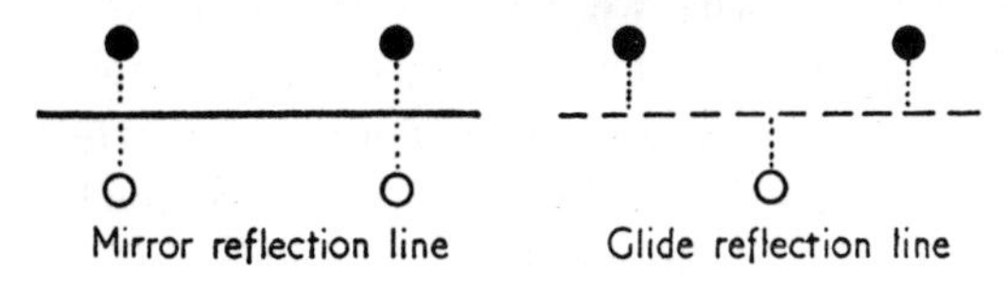

FIG. 69.

We then have to find which combinations of these symmetry elements are consistent with the five fundamental plane lattices. Let us consider the square lattice. We may first have simply a 4-fold axis (□) at each point of the lattice (Fig. 70 (*a*)). This

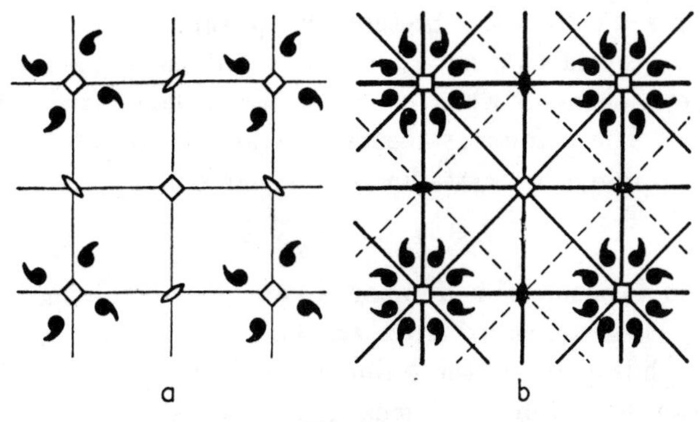

FIG. 70.

automatically introduces a 4-fold axis at the centre of each square 'cell' and 2-fold axes at the mid-points of the sides. Any point placed in the plane is repeated in the manner shown as sets of four points (commas) arranged around each point of the lattice. We could, however, also make the pattern symmetrical across each side of the square as at (*b*), by making the edges of the cells mirror reflection lines. This combination of 4-fold axes and mirror reflection lines turns a single point into a group of eight points around each lattice point. By finding all the permissible combinations of symmetry with the various 2-dimensional lattices we arrive at a total of seventeen *plane groups*, which form the basis of all 2-dimensional patterns (Fig. 71).

It will be noticed that in order to describe the symmetry of 2-dimensional patterns we have introduced two new ideas. (i) We have a new kind of symmetry element involving translation; this would be meaningless if applied to the faces of a crystal, which is a *finite* object. (ii) The symmetry elements themselves repeat at the points of the lattice. If a crystal has a number of symmetry elements these must necessarily pass through a point; otherwise, as in (i), they would produce infinite series of faces.

Symmetry of 3-*dimensional Arrangements of Points*

Finally, in order to find the possible 3-dimensional patterns of points which will represent the possible arrangements of atoms in crystals we have to discover all the combinations of symmetry elements which can be placed in the fourteen Bravais lattices. The symmetry elements available include not only those exhibited by crystalline solids, namely,

$$2, 3, 4, 6, \bar{1}, \bar{2}, \bar{3}, \bar{4}, \bar{6},$$

but also a considerable number of new types involving translations. These are called *screw axes* and *glide planes*.

The glide plane is the 3-dimensional analogue of the glide reflection line of our 2-dimensional patterns. As its name implies, it combines in one operation a movement with a reflection. If we imagine a point A (Fig. 72) on one side of a mirror moved first to A' and then reflected through the plane of the mirror to B, then we say that A is converted into B by the operation of the glide plane. The same operation performed on B would bring it to C, the translation being always a constant amount $\frac{1}{2}a$, where a is the unit translation of the lattice (see Fig. 35). A more complex type of glide plane could transform A into D, this involving translations of $\frac{1}{2}a+\frac{1}{2}c$, followed by reflection. If the unit translations a and c of the crystal lattice are not

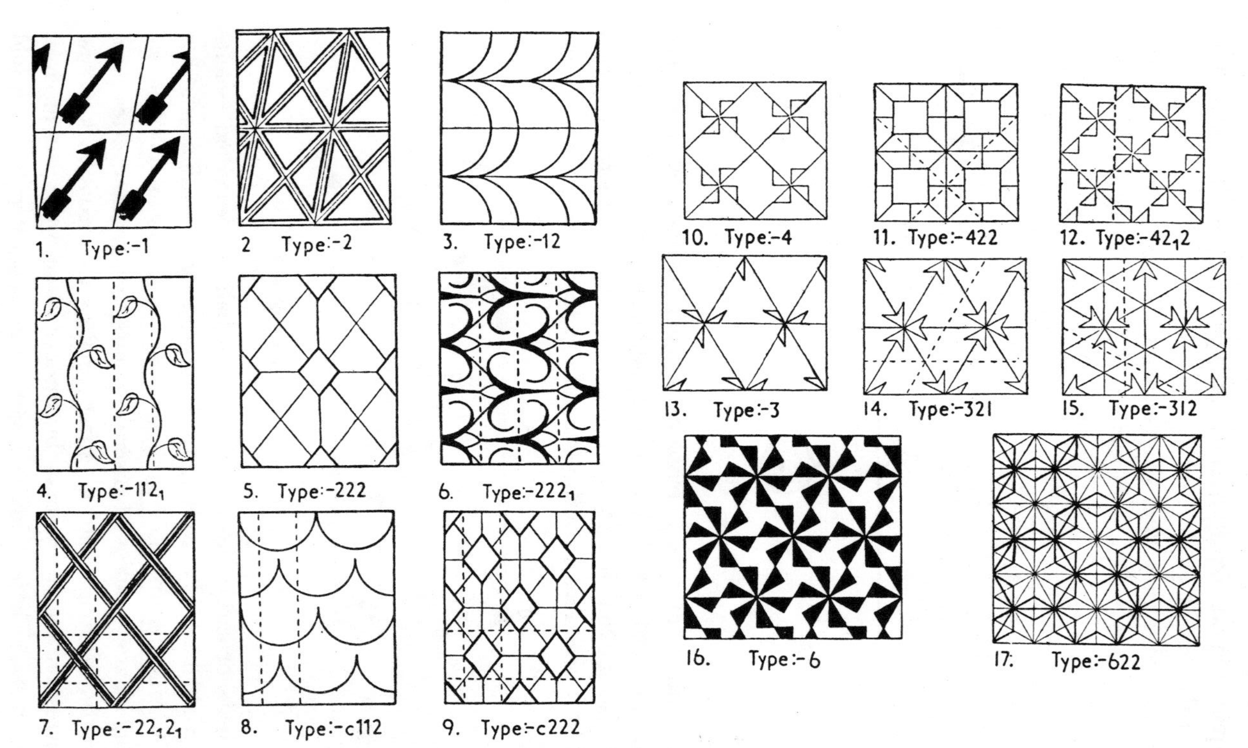

FIG. 71. Patterns illustrating the seventeen plane groups.

equivalent we clearly have three types of glide plane involving translations of $\frac{1}{2}a$, $\frac{1}{2}c$, and $\frac{1}{2}a+\frac{1}{2}c$.

The other new kind of symmetry element, the screw axis, derives its name from its relation to the ordinary screw thread.

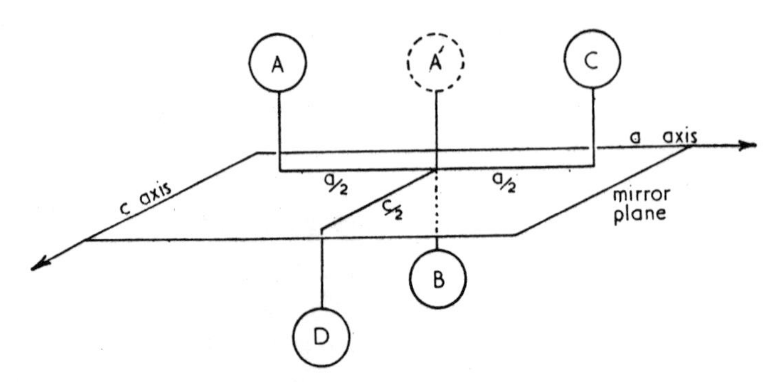

FIG. 72. The operation of a glide-plane.

A point rotated in a plane at a fixed distance from another point describes a circle, but if in addition to rotating the point is also moved forward at a rate proportional to the rotation then it describes a continuous path on the surface of a cylinder,

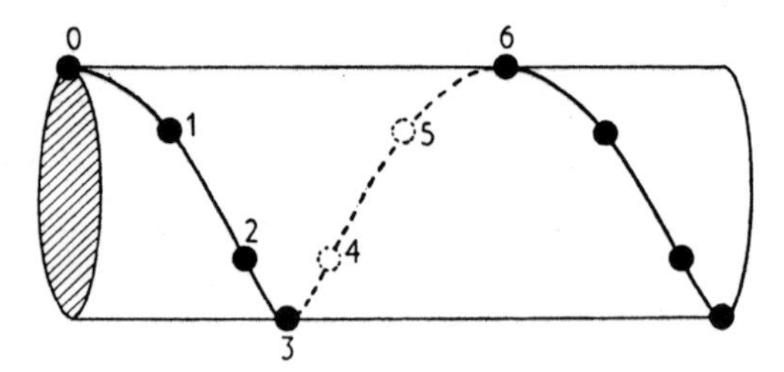

FIG. 73. The operation of a 6-fold screw-axis.

a helix or screw thread (Fig. 73). A helix is described as left- or right-handed according to the sense of the rotation, whether clockwise or anticlockwise. Instead of a continuous line we could have a series of discrete points, one marked after each rotation through $360°/n$. After n points we arrive back at one corresponding to the first, but moved along by x, the pitch of the helix. These points are said to be generated by an n-fold screw axis, those in Fig. 73 arising from the operation of a

6-fold screw axis (written 6_1). This interesting type of symmetry is exhibited by the spiral staircase (though a more correct term would be a helical staircase, since a spiral is a curved line on a plane), and also by the arrangements of leaves around the stems of certain plants (Fig. 74).

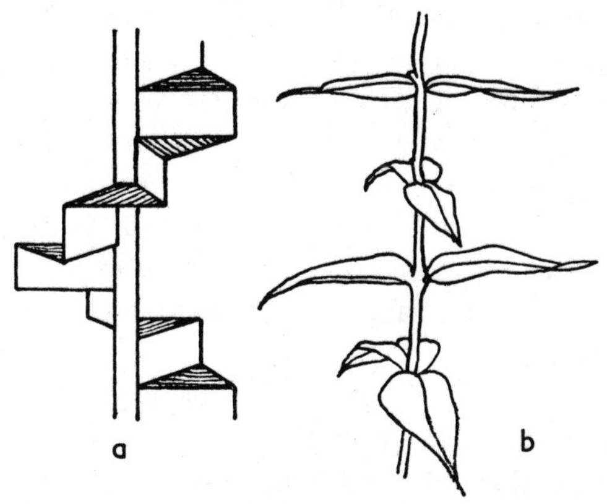

FIG. 74. Illustrating (*a*) 6_1 screw-axis (spiral staircase), and (*b*) 4_2 screw-axis (arrangement of leaves around stem of pentstemon, after Walter Crane).

Now for the 6-fold screw axis of Fig. 73 and in the spiral staircase each point (or stair) is related to the previous one by a rotation through 360°/6 and a simultaneous translation of $\frac{1}{6}x$, but in order to ensure that our original point repeats regularly at intervals of x along the direction of the axis it is not necessary that the translation is $\frac{1}{6}x$. It could have 2, 3, 4, or 5 times this value, the corresponding symbols being 6_2, 6_3, 6_4, and 6_5. A convenient way of showing the sets of points generated by such screw-axes is to represent them by sets of figures giving the heights of the points above the plane of the paper in terms of $\frac{1}{6}x$:

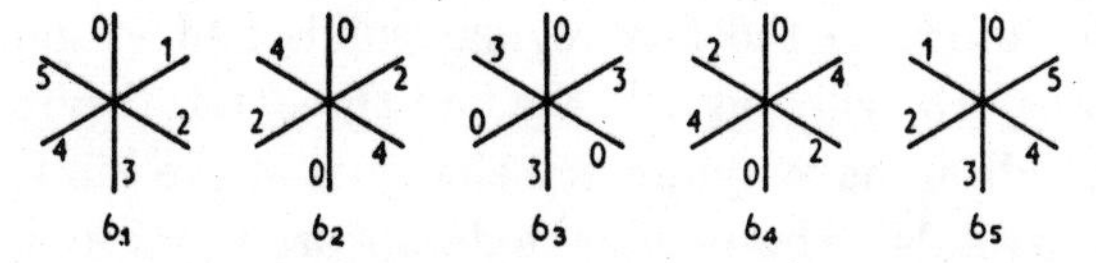

We start in each case at the top of the diagram (height 0) and proceed clockwise, rising n for an axis 6_n for each 60° of rotation. A point at height $(6+m)$ is a point m in the next repeat period, but since by definition each repeat period must contain the same arrangement of points this implies a point *m* in the original repeat period. It will be seen that 6_1 and 6_5, and 6_2 and 6_4, are related pairs corresponding to clockwise and anti-clockwise rotation.

We have seen that for the plane pattern there are five lattices (or axial systems) and seventeen permissible arrangements of symmetry elements consistent with these lattices, the seventeen plane-groups. It is evident that for 3-dimensional patterns the number of combinations of symmetry elements will be much greater. Instead of five lattices, there are the fourteen Bravais lattices, and in addition many new kinds of symmetry element are possible, the glide-planes and screw-axes that we have just been discussing.

During the years 1885–94 this problem was being studied independently by Fedorov in Russia, Schönfliess in Germany, and Barlow in England, and it was established that the number of combinations of symmetry elements consistent with the fourteen Bravais lattices is 230. The arrangement of the atoms in any crystal with a completely regular internal structure must possess the symmetry of one of these 230 *space-groups*. It is interesting that this space-group theory was worked out some twenty years before the experimental study of the atomic structures of crystals began, in 1912, with the first demonstration of the diffraction of X-rays by a crystal. However, as we note elsewhere, Barlow's studies had led him to predict at an even earlier date the structures of some simple crystals, structures which were subsequently confirmed by X-ray investigations.

After this brief discussion of symmetry it may interest the reader to return to the five regular solids and examine their symmetries. He will find that the first three, tetrahedron, cube, and octahedron, have symmetry elements of the kinds permissible for crystals. The regular dodecahedron and icosahedron, on the other hand, have both 3-fold and 5-fold axes of symmetry, and these are arranged in a way somewhat reminiscent of the arrangement of the 3-fold and 4-fold axes of a cube.

CHAPTER V

IONS AND IONIC CRYSTALS

A REMARKABLE feature of the material world is the variety of substances with which we are familiar in everyday life. They range from the petal of a flower or a butterfly's wing, through woods, rocks, metals, rubber, textiles (to name only a few solids), to liquids, gases, and smokes. All, from a horse to a 10 horse-power car, from a willow tree to a willow-pattern plate, are built of atoms. We now know about one hundred different kinds of atom, though many of these are extremely rare and some have only been produced 'artificially' in very small amounts. In fact, only a half-dozen or so different kinds of atoms are required to make most of the materials of the living world and not many more, though a different selection, to make the commoner rocks, sands, and soils of the earth's crust.

The reason for this extraordinary variety of materials lies, then, not so much in the number of different elements available but in the fact that atoms can link up to form arrangements ranging in complexity from simple molecules consisting of only two atoms to groupings so complicated that even today we have only the most rudimentary ideas of their structures. We can illustrate this point very simply by the series of compounds of carbon and hydrogen which begins with the gas methane (CH_4) and ends with the solid polymer polyethylene:

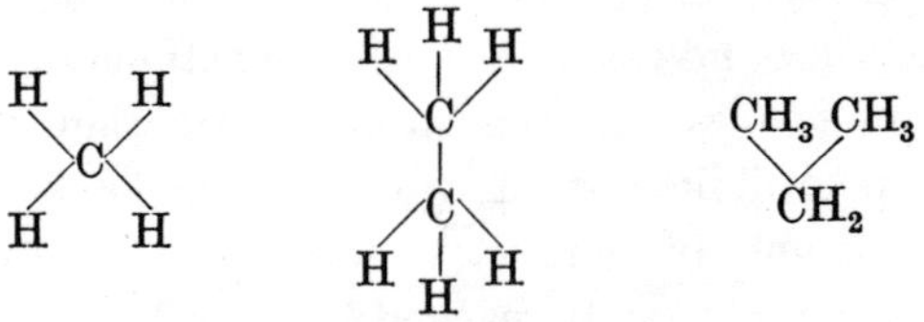

H H
C
H H

H H H
C
|
C
H H H

CH_3 CH_3
CH_2

to $CH_3—(CH_2)_n—CH_3$

and $(—CH_2—CH_2—CH_2—)_n$

polyethylene

This series, of general formula C_nH_{2n+2} (which approximates to C_nH_{2n} if n is very large), clearly has an indefinitely large number of members. Of these a considerable number have been characterized, and this number is limited only by the difficulty of separating the higher members, for if there is little difference in the length of chain of carbon atoms there is also little difference in physical properties. Up to the third member (which we may write for short C_3) there is only one molecule corresponding to a given formula, but from C_4 onwards another complication enters, namely, the possibility of linking the carbon atoms in different ways:

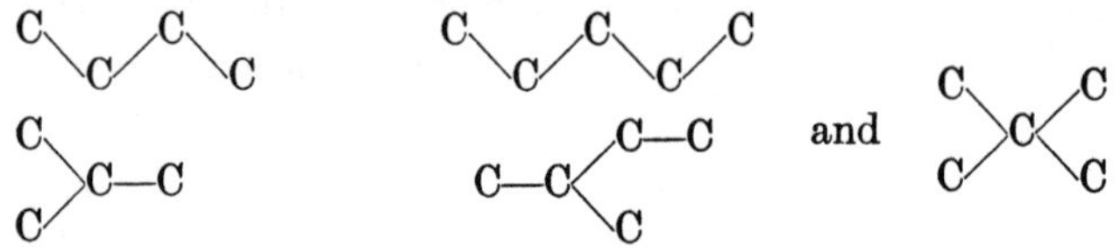

and

C_4: 2 ways C_5: 3 ways

Then, there is another infinite series of compounds in which there are closed rings of carbon atoms (*a*) and finally the mixed types (*b*).

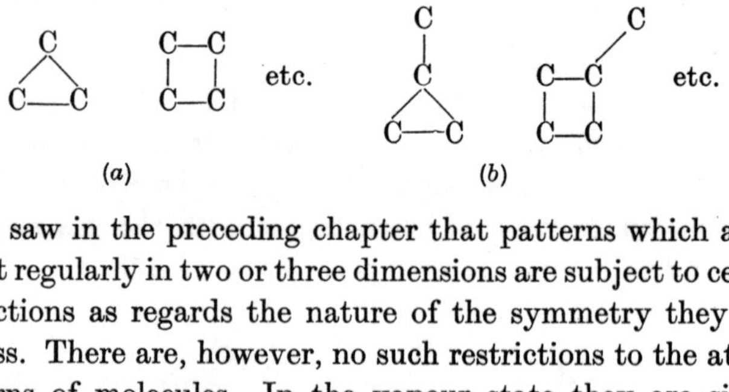

etc. etc.

(*a*) (*b*)

We saw in the preceding chapter that patterns which are to repeat regularly in two or three dimensions are subject to certain restrictions as regards the nature of the symmetry they may possess. There are, however, no such restrictions to the atomic patterns of molecules. In the vapour state they are simply isolated groups of linked atoms which do not have to conform to any requirements of symmetry, and in the crystalline state the molecules can always be packed in accordance with one of the fourteen Bravais lattices, whatever their size or shape. It is simply a matter of packing together objects of a particular shape; if the shape is awkward the packing may not be very good. The whole arrangement may, or may not, possess some symmetry, whether the individual molecule possesses symmetry or not. Some simple molecules have high symmetry, but in general the greater the complexity of the molecule the less likely is the molecule to possess any symmetry at all.

In this chapter and the next we shall attempt to show the structural principles in certain selected groups of compounds. Our treatment will be in no way systematic, the choice of examples being decided by their suitability for illustrating particular kinds of structures and, what is more important, by the fact that more is known of the structures of some groups of compounds than of others. Before we proceed any further, however, it may be advisable to say a little about the kinds of forces which hold atoms together in materials of different kinds.

The Structure of the Atom

First, a word about the scale of the patterns we shall be considering. However familiar we may be with words such as atom and atomic it is unlikely that we shall ever have any real appreciation of the minute size of atoms. A convenient unit when dealing with atoms is the Ångström unit, 1/100,000,000th part of a centimetre (10^{-8} cm.). Since the radii of atoms are of the order of one or two Ångström units it follows that a row of about one hundred million atoms would extend over about one inch, or about one hundred thousand would correspond to the thickness of a cigarette paper.

Not only is an atom very small but it also has a complex internal structure. An atom consists of a central nucleus around which revolve one or more electrons. In the simplest and lightest atom, that of hydrogen, there is one such electron, in a helium atom two, and so on up to 102 in an atom of Nobelium. Each electron carries unit negative charge ($-e$) and the nucleus carries a positive charge which balances that of all the planetary electrons. Practically the whole of the mass of an atom resides in the nucleus, and it is the nucleus carrying a particular charge which is characteristic of a given chemical element. If the nuclear charge is $+8$ the atom is an atom of oxygen; if it is $+79$ it is an atom of gold. It is with changes in the charge and mass of the nucleus that present-day atomic physics is concerned; a change in nuclear charge implies a transmutation of one chemical element into another.

As the number of planetary electrons increases they arrange themselves in groups (or shells) which can contain certain maximum numbers of electrons. Ordinary chemical reactions, as opposed to nuclear reactions, are concerned with loss, gain, or rearrangement of these planetary electrons, and the ease with which these processes occur depends on the electronic structures of the atoms. Hydrogen, with a single planetary or valency electron, is quite reactive chemically, but helium, with two electrons, is chemically inert, the group of two electrons having a considerable stability. The next element, lithium, with three valency electrons can, like hydrogen, give up one electron to form a singly charged positive ion. The succeeding elements:

	Be	B	C	N	O	F
Electronic structure .	2, 2	2, 3	2, 4	2, 5	2, 6	2, 7

all form numerous compounds, but when this second group of electrons contains 8, as in neon (2, 8), we again find great chemical inertness. Neon, like helium, forms no chemical compounds, and this inertness is found in a number of other elements, argon (2, 8, 8), krypton (2, 8, 18, 8), and xenon (2, 8, 18, 18, 8). As a result of this marked stability of certain completed groups of electrons we find a certain similarity in the chemical properties of elements which have the same numbers of electrons in their outermost shells. Thus,

Li (2, 1), Na (2, 8, 1), and K (2, 8, 8, 1)

have a definite family resemblance, and this fact was noted (by Mendeleev in 1869) long before the theory of the nuclear atom was put forward and was expressed in the Periodic Classification of the Elements.

Types of Chemical Bonds

Each of the alkali metals, lithium, sodium, and potassium, has one electron more than an inert gas (He, Ne, and A respectively), and the elements following them have two electrons more than the inert gases:

				He	2	Li	2, 1	Be	2, 2
O	2, 6	F	2, 7	Ne	2, 8	Na	2, 8, 1	Mg	2, 8, 2
S	2, 8, 6	Cl	2, 8, 7	A	2, 8, 8	K	2, 8, 8, 1	Ca	2, 8, 8, 2

The elements immediately preceding the inert gases have one electron fewer than the inert gases. The importance of the stable electronic structures of the inert gases lies in the fact that atoms close to these in the Periodic Classification strive to attain the electronic structures of the appropriate inert gases. They can do this in two essentially different ways.

The chlorine atom, with seven electrons in its outer shell, can take up an additional electron and in this way acquire the same outer electronic structure as the inert gas argon. It now carries a charge of -1 and is called an *ion*, this term being applied to any atom (or group of atoms) which has a charge, either positive or negative. Elements such as K, Na, or Li with one electron in the outer shell can reach an inert gas structure by losing one electron and becoming positive ions. A crystal of common salt is simply a large number of Na^+ and Cl^- ions, equal numbers of each, which are held together by their charges. We shall consider shortly how the ions arrange themselves in three dimensions; it is a question of packing together ions which we can regard as charged spheres, and the overriding principle is that as far as possible charges shall be neutralized locally. The maximum possible number of positive ions are grouped around each negative ion, and similarly for negative around positive ions. For a 2-dimensional packing of equal numbers of ions of the same size the arrangement shown in Fig. 75 (*a*) would give each ion the maximum number of neighbours of opposite charge. In a 3-dimensional structure the actual number of neighbours around each ion depends on the relative sizes of the ions, as already mentioned in our discussion of the closest packing of spheres.

The element sodium is a soft white metal. In a piece of sodium we can visualize sodium ions like those in common salt, but instead of each Na atom having given up an electron to a Cl atom to form Na^+ and Cl^- ions each sodium atom has contributed one electron to a sort of electron gas which might be described as a negatively charged cement holding together the positively charged sodium ions (Fig. 75 (*b*)). It is the presence of these free electrons which makes the metal a good conductor

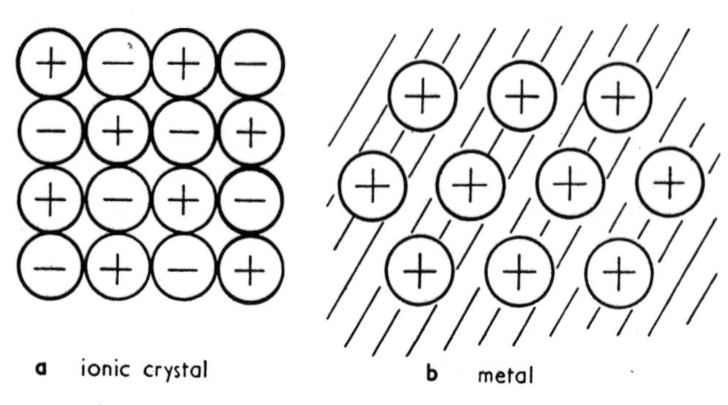

Fig. 75.

of heat and electricity as compared with an ionic crystal like sodium chloride which is an insulator.

Instead of gaining one electron and becoming an ion able to combine with positively charged ions of elements like sodium, the chlorine atom can reach the stable argon structure in another

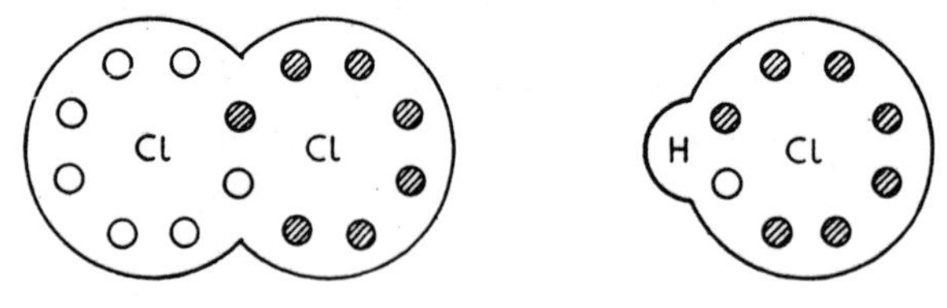

Fig. 76.

way. It can gain a share in another electron by sharing one of its electrons with an atom which also has one to contribute (Fig. 76). Although there are only fourteen valency electrons in the system Cl—Cl it appears that the central pair of electrons functions as part of the electronic systems of both atoms, and both atoms are satisfied. The importance of this *sharing* of electrons between atoms is that it can take place between all kinds of atoms provided that one or both of the atoms can supply the necessary electrons, and one of the more remarkable features of chemistry is the way in which almost all kinds of atoms combine together to form so many different compounds. In the examples of Fig. 76 each atom provides one of the electrons of the shared pair, but this is not essential; both can be provided by one of the atoms if the other has room in its outer shell for an additional pair of electrons. For example, nitrogen can form the stable ammonia molecule by sharing three electrons with three different hydrogen atoms, but the NH_3 molecule so formed can still use the pair of unshared electrons to form a further bond, as in the many 'ammines' it forms with metallic salts (e.g. $[Cu(NH_3)_4]SO_4$, $[Co(NH_3)_6]Cl_3$).

When a number of electron-pair bonds are formed by an atom they are inclined to one another at definite angles. In the molecule of boron trichloride, for example, the three chlorine atoms lie in the same plane as the boron atom, so that the molecule has the form of an equilateral triangle. The molecule of PCl_3, on the other hand, has a pyramidal shape, with the phosphorus atom at the apex. Some molecules X—A—X are straight, others are angular, and in general we may say that the difference is due to the presence or absence of one or more pairs of unshared electrons which behave, as regards the disposition of the bonds, as if they occupy the positions in which further bonds could be formed. This is in marked contrast to ionic bonds, for in an ionic crystal the ions of one kind arrange themselves around an ion of opposite charge in the most symmetrical way possible in space, namely, two on opposite sides of the ion, three at the corners of an equilateral triangle, four at the apices of a regular tetrahedron, and so on.

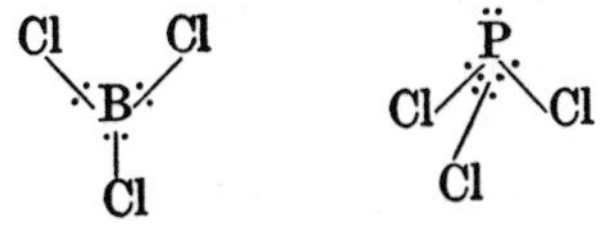

We have mentioned that the element chlorine, which is a gas at ordinary temperatures and atmospheric pressure, consists of molecules Cl_2 in which the atoms are joined by electron-pair or *covalent* bonds. If the gas is cooled sufficiently it liquefies, and at a still lower temperature it solidifies to a crystalline solid. In both the liquid and the solid there are the same Cl_2 molecules, but there are obviously forces of some kind between these chemically stable molecules, forces very much weaker than those between the atoms forming a molecule. We need not go into the origin of these forces; it is sufficient for our purpose to note that after atoms have combined to form a stable molecule they can still exert weak attractive forces on atoms of other molecules and that these forces are responsible for the cohesion of crystals built of discrete molecules. They are called van der Waals forces, after the Dutch physicist who modified the equation of state of a perfect gas ($PV = RT$) to take account of these attractive forces and of the volume occupied by the molecules by introducing the terms a/v^2 and $-b$ respectively.

Although we have talked about four distinct types of bond, ionic, metallic, covalent, and van der Waals, this is an over-simplification. It is known that in many molecules and crystals the bonds are intermediate in nature between these extreme types. For example, if two identical atoms such as Cl unite to form a molecule Cl_2 it is reasonable to suppose that the two electrons forming the bond between them are shared equally, but in the case of two unlike atoms this is not so. One atom can exert a greater pull on the electrons than the other with the result that the effective centre of the assembly of positive charges is separated from that of the negative charges in the molecule. Such a molecule may be thought of as the electrical equivalent of a magnet, and is described as *polar*. A simple but important example is the water molecule. The effect of the two hydrogen atoms is to distort the arrangement of the electrons around the oxygen atom in such a way that the molecule behaves as if it had a tetrahedral distribution of charges (Fig. 77). As a result of these rather weak charges a water molecule tends to attract only four nearest neighbours when it is present in crystals. These neighbours are arranged tetrahedrally, and

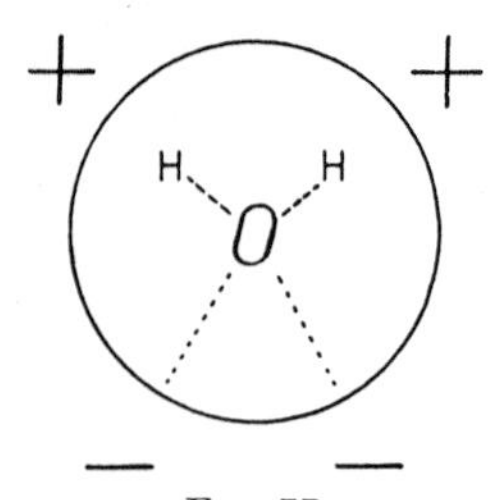

FIG. 77.

we shall see later that this leads to a very simple, and very open, structure for crystalline water (ice). It appears that the hydrogen atoms play an essential part in these links between water molecules and they are described as *hydrogen bonds* or *hydrogen bridges*.

In the next chapter we shall describe some of the ways in which atoms forming directed electron-pair bonds build up the complex structures found in crystalline solids. We shall conclude this chapter by illustrating some of the simpler types of ionic crystal.

The Structures of Ionic Crystals

As we have said, the problem is essentially one of packing together charged spheres. A crystal of a simple salt such as NaCl consists of equal numbers of positively and negatively charged ions. It might be expected that the simplest structure would arise for a salt AX if the ions A and X are equal in size, the spherical ions forming a close-packed assembly in which each would have twelve neighbours of the other sort, but we shall see shortly that there is a slight complication, of a purely geometrical nature, in this case. The most stable arrangement is that in which each ion has the maximum number of neighbours of opposite sign. Let us suppose that the X ions are larger than the A ions; in NaCl the radii are: Na^+, 0·95 Å., Cl^-, 1·8 Å. Since we must have equal numbers of A and X ions in the crystal, the maximum number of neighbours is the maximum number of the larger X ions which can be placed in contact with one of the smaller A ions. It would, of course, be possible to group a larger number of the small A ions around X, but this number of neighbours (coordination number) would be impossible for the larger X ions around A. The number of ions of one kind which we can place around another obviously depends on the relative sizes of the ions, but the coordination numbers found in simple ionic crystals are also limited to those which correspond to highly symmetrical arrangements of neighbours, as already mentioned.

The relative sizes of Na^+ and Cl^- permit six of the latter to be placed around Na^+ at the corners of an octahedron, and the simplest structure in which this can be realized was described by Barlow in 1883, some thirty years before it was actually deduced by the methods of X-ray crystallography (Fig. 78). As the sizes of A and X become more nearly equal a higher coordination number is to be expected, and certain salts AX

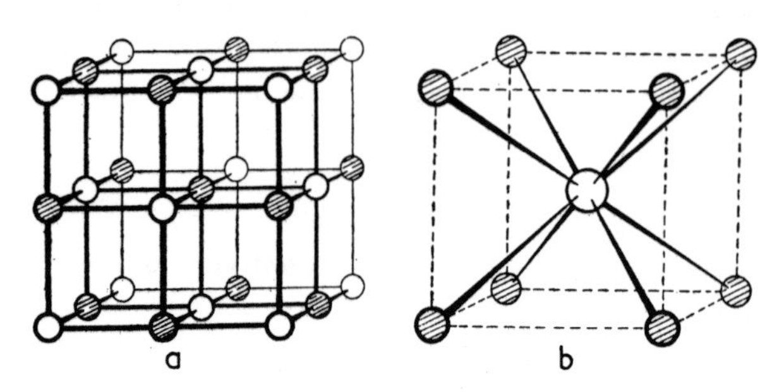

FIG. 78. The crystal structure of (*a*) sodium chloride, (*b*) caesium chloride.

have a structure in which each ion is surrounded by eight of opposite charge arranged at the corners of a cube (Fig. 78 (*b*)).

For ions A and X of equal size we might expect a coordination number 12, as in the closest packing of equal spheres. However, if we start to make a close-packed layer of ions A and X we find that as soon as we have placed six X around A each X already has two X neighbours, so that it is impossible to have a close-packed structure in which each A ion is surrounded by twelve X ions.

In the two structures which we have just described there are equal numbers of oppositely charged ions, and the following are some of the salts which crystallize with these structures:

NaCl structure: All the alkali halides except CsCl, CsBr, and CsI; AgF, AgCl, AgBr (and many oxides, e.g. MgO, CaO).

CsCl structure: CsCl, CsBr, CsI, TlCl, TlBr.

Although CsCl crystallizes at room temperature with the structure of Fig. 78 (*b*) its structure changes at 445° C. to the NaCl structure. This property of crystallizing with more than one structure is not confined to ionic compounds. Many elements and compounds have this property, which is called *polymorphism*. In some cases there is a definite temperature at which one form changes into the other, as, for example, with the two forms of sulphur. In other cases one form is stable at all temperatures under atmospheric pressure. A substance of the first kind is described as *enantiotropic* and of the second kind *monotropic*. Many examples of enantiotropic substances are known where the transition point is well above ordinary temperatures, and yet both forms are found as minerals. For example, the transition point for the two forms of ZnS is around 1020° C., below which temperature one form (the mineral wurtzite) should revert to the stable form (zinc blende or sphalerite). Even more striking is the fact that carbon is monotropic, and at atmospheric pressure diamond is the unstable form at all temperatures (graphite being the stable polymorph), though this does not appear to reduce the market value of diamonds.

The explanation lies in the fact that the actual change of one polymorph into another involves a rearrangement of the atoms in the solid state. For some polymorphic changes this necessitates only small movements of atoms or molecules relative to one another; only a small impetus is required, and the process takes place readily. In other cases the change corresponds to a radical rearrangement of the atoms, requiring, for example, the breaking of primary chemical bonds and the re-joining of atoms into a different arrangement, as for the change from diamond to graphite. Such a change never takes place under ordinary conditions, and both polymorphs can be kept for indefinite periods.

The term *allotropy* has been used to cover all cases where an element exists in more than one form, the word form including differences in crystal structure (as for sulphur, phosphorus, or carbon) and also differences such as that between the molecule of oxygen O_2 and that of ozone, O_3. There would seem to be little need to retain this term, since apart from the case of ozone and oxygen, where there are different chemical properties, all examples of allotropy are preferably described as polymorphism.

We shall meet other examples of this phenomenon in this chapter and the next.

Salts AX_2

If the formula of a salt is of the type AX_2, then assuming that each A atom has the same number of X neighbours and each X atom the same number of A neighbours it follows that the former number (the coordination number of A) must be

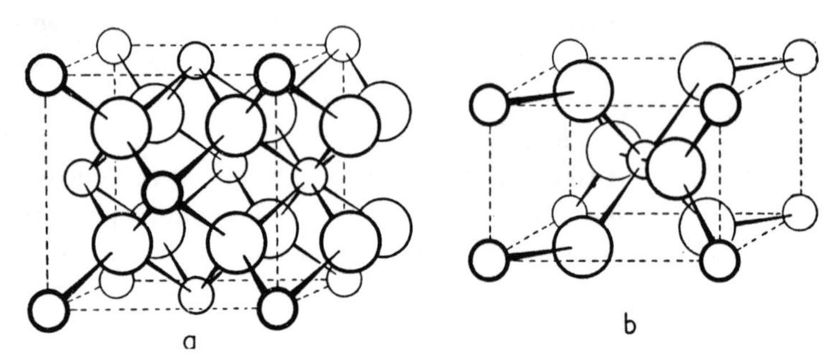

FIG. 79. The crystal structure of (*a*) fluorite, CaF_2, (*b*) rutile, TiO_2. The smaller circles represent metal ions.

twice the latter. For example, if each A is surrounded by six X, each X must be surrounded by three A to make the ratio A:X equal to 1:2. Two structures adopted by a number of ionic compounds AX_2 are the *fluorite structure* (named after the mineral fluorite, CaF_2) and the *rutile structure* (after the mineral rutile, TiO_2). These structures are illustrated in Fig. 79.

In the fluorite structure each Ca^{2+} ion is surrounded by eight F^- ions arranged at the corners of a cube, and each F^- by four Ca^{2+} at the corners of a tetrahedron. In the rutile structure each metal ion (Ti^{4+}) has six O^{2-} ions as nearest neighbours, arranged at the corners of an octahedron, and each O^{2-} ion has three Ti^{4+} neighbours at the corners of an equilateral triangle.

It is interesting to notice here two ways in which the same geometrical pattern of atoms is made to serve for compounds with more complex chemical formulae. If ions of two metals are of about the same size they can crystallize with F^- or O^{2-} ions to form a complex halide or oxide. Some compounds of this kind have the same structure as the simple halides or oxides but with the two kinds of metal ion arranged at random in the metal-ion positions of the simple structure. Examples are:

$KLaF_4$ with a random fluorite structure,
$FeSbO_4$ with a random rutile structure.

In other compounds of this sort the various ions still occupy the positions of the ions in the simple structure but the two (or

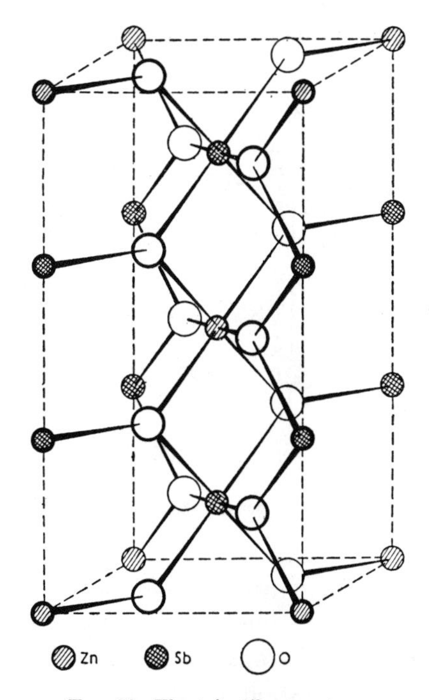

FIG. 80. The trirutile structure.

more) kinds of metal ion are arranged in a regular way. This occurs in $ZnSb_2O_6$ which has the structure illustrated in Fig. 80. Owing to the regular arrangement of the Zn and Sb atoms the repeat distance of the atomic pattern along the vertical axis is three times as great as in the simple rutile structure, and accordingly the structure is called the '*trirutile*' structure.

A rather similar relationship exists between the structures of zinc blende, ZnS, and two other minerals, chalcopyrite, $CuFeS_2$, and stannite, Cu_2FeSnS_4. In zinc blende the atoms of Zn and S occupy alternately the positions of the C atoms in the diamond structure (Fig. 90, p. 114). In $CuFeS_2$ the Cu and Fe atoms replace the Zn atoms in the ZnS structure in a regular manner, and in Cu_2FeSnS_4 there is a further regular replacement of one-half of the Fe atoms of $CuFeS_2$ by Sn atoms. Here again the same atomic pattern serves for compounds with quite different kinds of chemical formulae, which at first sight might be expected to have much more complicated structures.

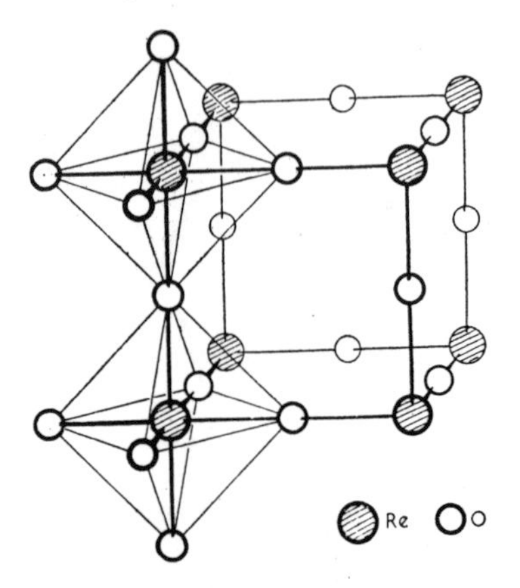

FIG. 81. The crystal structure of ReO_3.

Salts AX_3

We shall mention here only one structure of a compound AX_3, the very simple structure illustrated in Fig. 81, which represents the arrangement of atoms in the oxide ReO_3 and certain trifluorides. This illustration suggests a way of describing these simple ionic crystal structures which has some advantages over the conventional type of diagram in which the positions of the centres of all the atoms are indicated as small circles.

Ionic Crystal Structures and the Open Packing of Polyhedra

If we focus our attention on a metal ion in Fig. 81 we see that its six immediate neighbours form an octahedral group AX_6. Each X ion is shared between two A ions, or alternatively, each corner of the octahedron is joined to the corner of another octahedron. We can think of such a structure as a system of octahedra, each of which is joined to six others by its corners, that is, the structure is an 'open packing' of octahedra. It is rather difficult to visualize more complex structures in this way as 3-dimensional systems of polyhedra but it is often possible to pick out, for example, strings or layers of octahedra and to

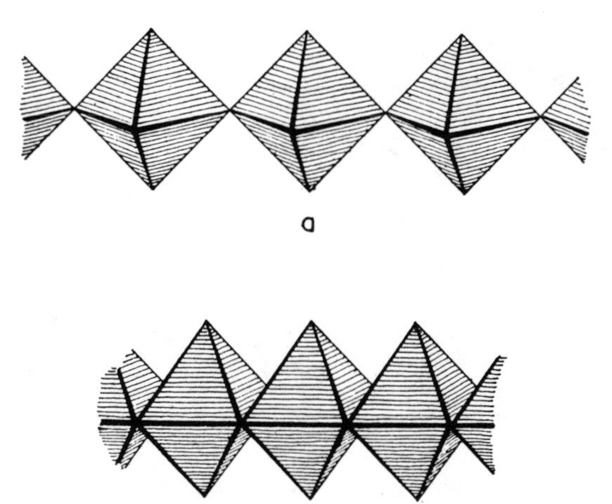

FIG. 82. Chains of octahedra sharing (*a*) two opposite corners, (*b*) two opposite edges.

see how these join up by further sharing of corners or edges to form the 3-dimensional structures.

The two simplest ways of joining octahedra AX_6 to form infinite chains are (*a*) by sharing a pair of opposite corners, and (*b*) by sharing a pair of opposite edges (Fig. 82). It can easily be verified that the compositions of such chains are (*a*) AX_5 and (*b*) AX_4. (In the first case two of the X atoms of each octahedron are shared between two octahedra and therefore count as $\frac{1}{2}X$, so that we have $4X+2(\frac{1}{2}X) = 5X$; in the second case four of the six X atoms are shared in this way giving $2X+4(\frac{1}{2}X) = 4X$.)

Chains of type (*b*), of which another view is shown in Fig. 83 (*a*), can be joined along their lengths by placing edges of octahedra in contact. The double chain so formed has the composition AX_3, and such units occur in crystals of the 'double chloride' NH_4CdCl_3, which at one time would have been regarded as a crystalline mixture and formulated $NH_4Cl.CdCl_2$ (Figs. 83 (*c*) and 101 (*g*)). If the process is continued the result is a layer of octahedra (Fig. 83 (*d*)) having the composition AX_2. This type of layer is found in crystals of many dihalides and

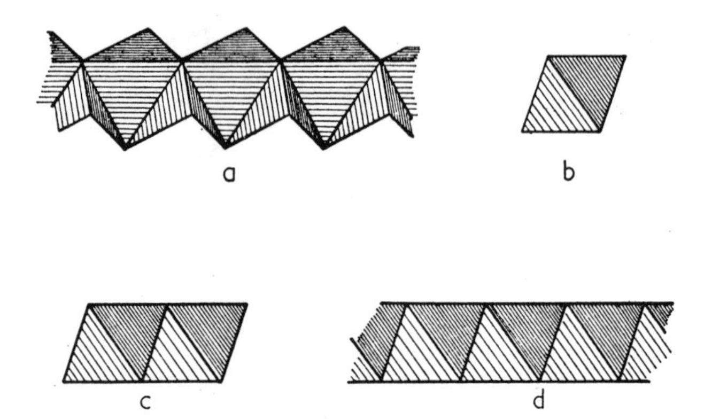

Fig. 83. (*a*) octahedral groups AX_6 sharing edges to form a chain AX_4, (*b*) end-on view of chain, (*c*) and (*d*), end-on views of double chain AX_3 and layer AX_2.

some disulphides (e.g. CdI_2, $CdCl_2$, SnS_2). The layer may be regarded as a 'two-dimensional molecule', and in the crystal the layers are piled on top of one another and held together only by the weak van der Waals forces to which we referred earlier. The simplest AX_2 structure built of these layers of octahedral AX_6 groups is that of CdI_2, which is illustrated in the conventional way as a system of linked Cd and I atoms in Fig. 84. Part of a layer is shown in plan in Fig. 85 (*a*), the metal atoms (in the plane of the paper) occupying the interstices between I atoms which lie in two parallel planes above and below that of the metal atoms. If one-third of the metal atoms are removed from a layer of this kind, as in Fig. 85 (*b*), leaving only those at the corners of a hexagonal net, the composition of the layer becomes AX_3. This type of layer is the basis of the structures of a number of trihalides (e.g. $CrCl_3$, BiI_3) and also of $Al(OH)_3$. It is also illustrated as a packing of octahedra in Fig. 88 (*c*), Plate XII.

Comparison of Figs. 85 and 42 (p. 53) shows that the halogen atoms in these layers are arranged in closest packing, with the metal atoms A in the octahedral interstices, so that there are various ways of stacking these composite layers or sandwiches (X—A—X) on one another to give different kinds of closest

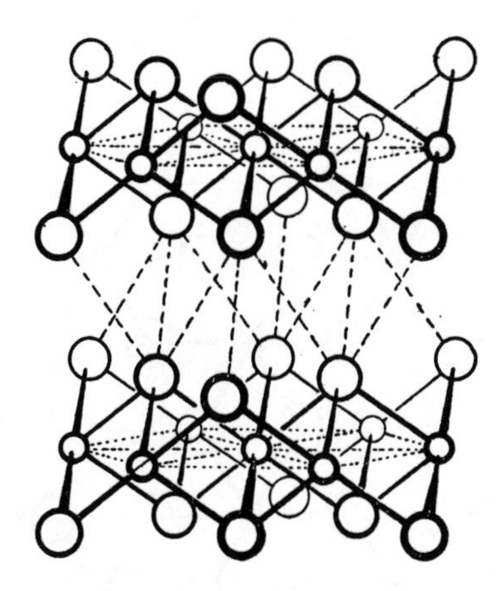

FIG. 84. The (layer) structure of cadmium iodide. Small circles represent metal atoms.

packing, as described in Chapter III. In the two simplest structures the halogen atoms are arranged in hexagonal and cubic closest packing, and both of the corresponding structures are found for AX_2 and AX_3 halides.

	Close-packing of halogen atoms	
	Hexagonal	*Cubic*
AX_2	CdI_2	$CdCl_2$
AX_3	$CrBr_3$ ($FeCl_3$)	$CrCl_3$

These close-packed structures can be represented diagrammatically by showing the type of layer *A*, *B*, or *C* (see p. 52

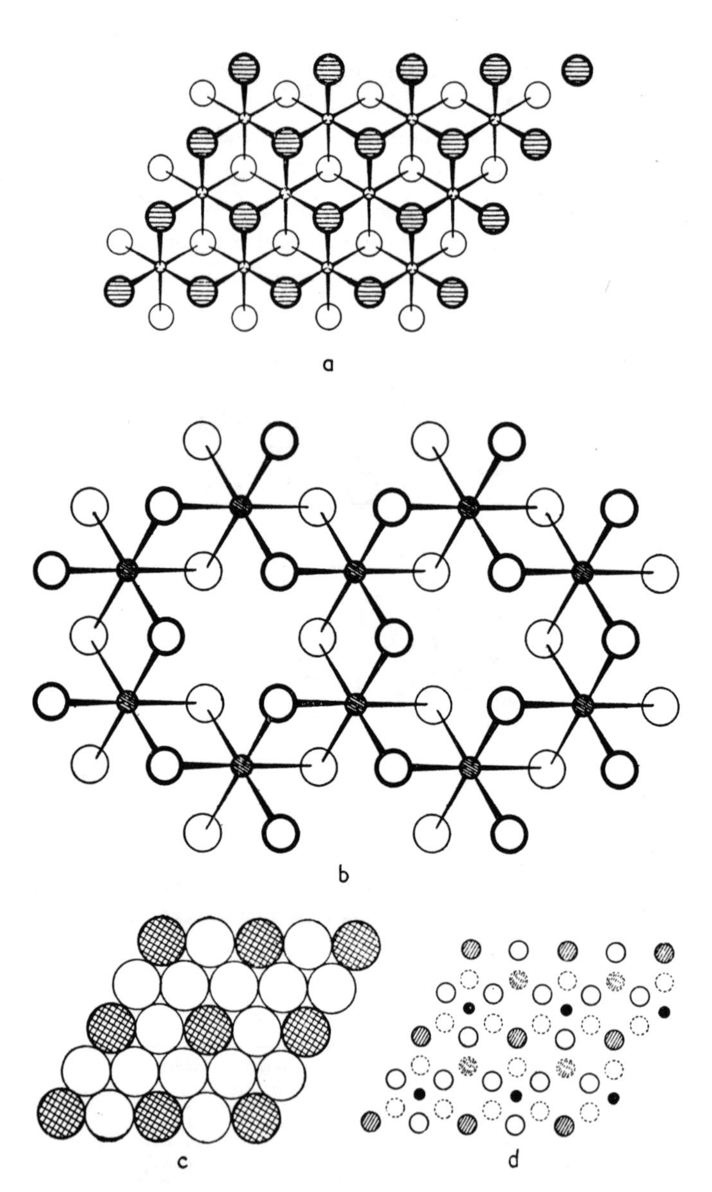

FIG. 85. Atomic arrangement in (*a*) CdI_2 and (*b*) BiI_3 layers. (*c*) Close-packed layer AX_3 of atoms of two kinds, (*d*) two adjacent layers of type (*c*) (full and dotted circles) showing the positions midway between the layers for metal atoms (small black circles) within octahedra of X atoms.

and Fig. 42) and the sequence of layers:

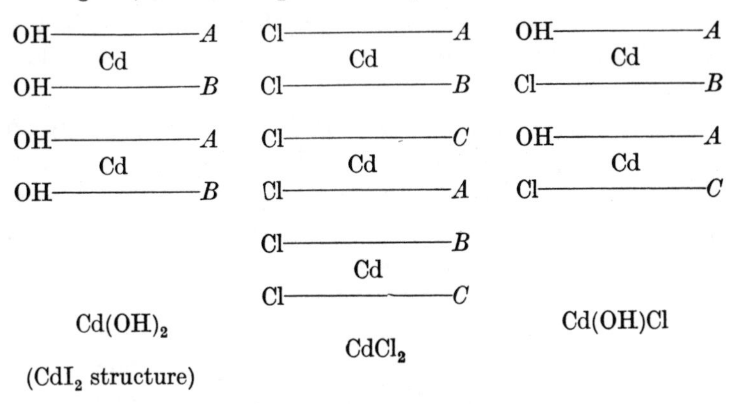

At the right is shown the structure of cadmium hydroxychloride, at one time written $Cd(OH)_2 . CdCl_2$. In this compound there are alternate layers of OH and Cl, so that each cadmium atom is surrounded by three OH and three Cl, as compared with six OH in $Cd(OH)_2$ and six Cl in $CdCl_2$. We see, therefore, that Cd(OH)Cl is in no sense a mixture of the hydroxide and chloride but a compound with a definite structure of its own. It will be noticed that the sequence of layers in this compound corresponds to 'double hexagonal' closest packing (p. 53) whereas the hydroxide and chloride are examples of hexagonal and cubic closest packing respectively. The reasons for these rather subtle differences between compounds so closely related as CdI_2 and $CdCl_2$ are not understood, nor indeed is the reason for the adoption of hexagonal closest packing by some metals while others are cubic closest packed.

In many complex halides and oxides the halogen or oxygen ions are close-packed and metal ions occupy various proportions of the octahedral and/or tetrahedral holes. In this way a great variety of crystalline compounds with quite different kinds of chemical formulae have structures based on the same arrangement of halogen or oxygen ions. The number of octahedral holes in a close-packed assembly is equal to the number of spheres. In the cadmium chloride structure one-half of these holes are occupied by metal atoms, in the $CrCl_3$ structure, one-third. In α-Al_2O_3 (corundum, sapphire) and α-Fe_2O_3 (the mineral haematite, jewellers' rouge) there are metal ions in two-thirds of the octahedral holes in a hexagonal close-packing of oxygen ions.

Another kind of structure becomes possible when there are metal ions of more than one kind in addition to halogen or oxygen ions. This type of compound used to be called a 'mixed' halide or oxide and formulated, for example, as $KF.MgF_2$ or $CaO.TiO_2$. The term 'complex halide' or 'complex oxide' is now to be preferred, since such crystals are not mixtures but have structures which are quite different from those of the component compounds. We saw that a simple halide such as KF in which the ions are of the same size does not form a close-packed structure because in any close-packed structure the potassium ions would have at least two similar ions as nearest neighbours. If, however, there is a smaller proportion of K^+ ions (e.g. K : 3F) a close-packed structure can be formed in which K^+ is surrounded completely by F^- ions. For example, this is true if we superpose layers like that of Fig. 85 (*c*) in the way shown at (*d*). Between each pair of close-packed layers there are positions for small metal ions (the black circles in Fig. 85 (*d*)), and the composition of the whole crystal, which is of the form $A_xB_yC_{3x}$, depends on the proportion of these octahedral holes which are occupied (compare $CdCl_2$ and $CrCl_3$). If all are occupied the formula is ABX_3, and $KMgF_3$ is an example of a complex halide of this kind. In $Cs_3As_2Cl_9$ and K_2PtCl_6 two-thirds and one-half respectively of the B positions are occupied. This close structural relationship between three salts with apparently quite different types of formulae is more easily seen if we write the formulae:

$$K_3Mg_3F_9, \quad Cs_3As_2Cl_9, \quad \text{and} \quad K_3Pt_{\frac{3}{2}}Cl_9.$$

A large family of complex oxides in which the oxygen ions are close-packed includes $CaTiO_3$ (the mineral perovskite); all have the same structure as $KMgF_3$ or slightly distorted variants of it. In silicate minerals there is in most cases some form of close-packing of the oxygen ions, but we shall find it more convenient to describe their structures (in the next chapter) in terms of the way in which the $(Si,Al)O_4$ tetrahedra are linked together.

A more complicated kind of layer than that of the $CdCl_2$ structure, in this case a corrugated layer, can be built of the double strings of octahedra of Fig. 83 (*c*). It is illustrated in Fig. 86 (*a*), Plate XI. So far we have been considering how the chains of octahedra of Fig. 83 (*a*) can be joined up along their lengths to form double chains or layers. They can also be joined up to form extended 3-dimensional structures. One structure built of double chains is illustrated in Fig. 86 (*b*). Both the layer of Fig. 86 (*a*) and the 'honeycomb' structure of (*b*) are possible structures for compounds AX_2, and in fact they represent the structures of the two crystalline forms of AlO(OH), a compound intermediate, as regards chemical composition, between the oxide Al_2O_3 and the hydroxide $Al(OH)_3$. (In the hydroxyl group the H atom is so small that this OH group can be regarded as a spherical unit like the oxygen atom itself.)

Manganese dioxide, MnO_2, and some closely related compounds provide interesting examples of a number of structures which from the geometrical standpoint represent different ways of packing octahedra. The structural chemistry of MnO_2 is complicated by the fact that manganese is an element which can form ions Mn^{2+}, Mn^{3+}, and Mn^{4+}, as in the compounds:

$$Mn^{4+}: MnO_2$$

$$Mn^{3+}: Mn_2O_3,\ MnO(OH)$$

$$Mn^{2+}: Mn(OH)_2.$$

Suppose that some of the manganese ions in MnO_2 are in the form of Mn^{3+} instead of Mn^{4+}. Electrical neutrality can be maintained either by replacing a similar number of O^{2-} ions by OH^- or by *adding* the same number of K^+ ions, or other singly-charged ions, or half the number of Ca^{2+} ions, or similar ions. In the latter case the manganese-oxygen framework would carry a negative charge balanced by the positive ions in the interstices.

The structure of the ordinary form of MnO_2 is built from

chains of octahedra joined together as shown in Fig. 87 (*a*) to form a neutral framework of linked octahedra. This structure has already been illustrated in a different way in Fig. 79 (*b*). A second crystalline form (*b*) is built of double chains; this is the structure already illustrated for one of the forms of AlO(OH).

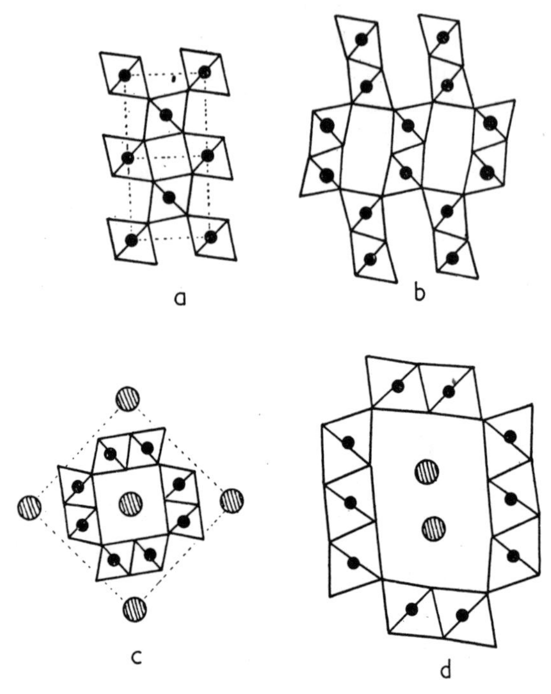

FIG. 87. Diagrammatic projections of structures based on single and multiple chains of octahedra viewed along the length of the chains. Large shaded circles represent Ba^{2+} ions in the interstices of the frameworks; small black circles represent manganese atoms at the centres of octahedra.

Material with this structure never has exactly the composition MnO_2, but always contains some 5 per cent. of impurities, including water. If large ions are present, more open structures can be formed, such as those shown at (*c*) or (*d*) in Fig. 87. The former contains K^+ or Ba^{2+} ions and shows 'ion exchange' like the zeolites (p. 128), and in the latter the even larger tunnels accommodate some Ba^{2+} ions and water molecules.

We have illustrated the structure of common salt in Fig. 78 (p. 96) as an assembly of ions. It can also be illustrated (Fig. 88 (*a*), Plate XII) as a packing of octahedra, since each Na^+ ion is surrounded octahedrally by six Cl^- and Cl^- similarly by six Na^+. If we remove one-half of the sodium ions from this structure we obviously have a possible structure for a compound AX_2. One simple way in which this can be done is shown in Fig. 88 (*b*). No dihalide is known with this structure but just as Cd(OH)Cl has a structure closely related to that of the dichloride so the hydroxychloride of copper, $Cu_2(OH)_3Cl$, has the structure of Fig. 88 (*b*). We saw that in Cd(OH)Cl the octahedral coordination group around each Cd consisted of 3 OH+ 3 Cl. In this copper compound it is not possible for all the Cu atoms to have the same environment because of the ratio of OH:Cl, and we find that one-half of the Cu atoms are surrounded by 4 OH+2 Cl and the remainder by 5 OH+Cl.

The reader may like to verify that another simple way of removing one-half of the sodium ions from the NaCl structure is to remove alternate layers perpendicular to a body-diagonal of the cubic unit cell (Fig. 78 (*a*)). If a model of this structure is set up so that a body-diagonal of the unit cell is vertical it will be seen that the ions are arranged in horizontal planes. Removal of alternate planes of sodium ions leaves a layer structure which is, in fact, the $CdCl_2$ structure which we have already derived in a different way.

These examples must suffice to illustrate how the structures of many solid compounds with apparently quite different types of formulae such as TiO_2, AlO(OH), and $Cu_2(OH)_3Cl$ can be regarded as variations on a particular structural theme, in the present instance the linking of octahedral groups through edges and corners. They also show how far we have advanced since the days when AlO(OH) was written $Al_2O_3 . H_2O$ and $Cu_2(OH)_3Cl$ as $3Cu(OH)_2 . CuCl_2$.

CHAPTER VI

FINITE AND INFINITE MOLECULES

In the last chapter we described the structures of some typical crystals built of ions. The negative ions were those of the lighter elements of the later groups of the Periodic Table, fluorine, chlorine, oxygen, and sulphur, and the positive ions were those of metals. We now wish to consider the structures of compounds formed by the non-metallic elements of the first set when they combine one with another. In these compounds we are concerned with bonds formed by the *sharing* of electrons, not by the transference of electrons to form ions.

The elements boron to fluorine of the first row of the Periodic Table have respectively three to seven electrons in the outermost shell (valency group), and we might have expected them to form these numbers of bonds in hydrides BH_3 to FH_7. Although boron forms a series of *halides* BX_3 it does not form a hydride BH_3; the hydrides of boron are peculiarly complex and will not be discussed here. The next element, carbon, forms CH_4 (as well as many more complex hydrides), but the highest hydrides formed by the remaining elements are NH_3, OH_2, and FH, that is, the element is forming 8-N bonds (N being the number of the Periodic Group). The formation of the hypothetical compounds NH_5, OH_6, and FH_7 (or the corresponding compounds NX_5, etc., where X is a halogen) with electron-pair bonds would mean the expansion of the electronic group to ten, twelve, or fourteen electrons, whereas by forming only 8-N bonds the valency group expands to eight electrons, the very stable arrangement found in the inert gas neon. Expansion of the valency group beyond the octet never takes place with these first-row elements, and nitrogen and oxygen also have another peculiarity, the preference for forming multiple bonds (by sharing four or six electrons in one bond) instead of single bonds in the elementary state. We shall return to this point shortly.

In addition to forming three bonds, as in NH_3, nitrogen can also imitate carbon by losing an electron and forming four tetrahedral bonds, as in the ammonium ion $(NH_4)^+$, but in no case does this element form more than four bonds.

The highest normal oxy-ions formed by these first-row elements are

$$BO_3^{3-} \qquad CO_3^{2-} \qquad NO_3^-$$

all having the form of equilateral triangles with B, C, or N at the centre. When we come to the elements of the second row we find that phosphorus forms pentahalides such as PF_5, PCl_5, and PBr_5, and sulphur forms SF_6, though we do not find a halogen compound of the type ClX_7; the only inter-halogen compound of this type is IF_7. We therefore have

	SiH_4	PH_3	SH_2	ClH	(8-*N* bonds)
but	SiF_4	PF_5	SF_6	—	(*N* bonds),

in which the elements are exhibiting valencies of 8-*N* and *N*. In their oxy-ions also these elements differ from those of the first row in forming tetrahedral ions

$$SiO_4^{4-} \qquad PO_4^{3-} \qquad SO_4^{2-} \qquad ClO_4^-$$

(in addition to numerous other oxy-ions), and in the case of silicon there is a very extensive structural chemistry based on the tetrahedral SiO_4 group.

As an introduction to the structural chemistry of these elements we shall devote short sections to the structures of the following:

(*a*) the elements,
(*b*) the highest normal oxides,
(*c*) some compounds of carbon,
(*d*) silicates,
(*e*) ice and hydrogen peroxide.

The Elements

The elements of Group 7, the halogens, with seven electrons in the outermost shell, can acquire a share in one additional electron by forming one electron-pair bond with another atom.

This leads to a molecule X_2 in which both atoms are satisfied, and the process of linking goes no farther. The first two halogens, fluorine and chlorine, are gases at ordinary temperature and pressure, bromine is a liquid, and iodine a solid. In all states of aggregation they all consist of such diatomic molecules. It is possible to break up these very stable molecules by heating the gases to a high temperature, but the single atoms thus formed recombine on cooling.

If we now turn to the atoms of the sixth Periodic family we find that these have six electrons in the outermost shell and accordingly they readily form two bonds. The first two elements of this family are oxygen and sulphur, one a gas and the other a solid at ordinary temperatures. For an atom forming two bonds there are two possibilities: the formation of closed rings or infinite chains. Ordinary crystalline sulphur consists of S_8 molecules which have the form of a puckered octagon (see Fig. 90). When crystalline sulphur is melted these S_8 rings tend to get broken open, the more so the higher the temperature, so that at higher temperatures molten sulphur contains a considerable proportion of fragmentary chains of various lengths. If molten sulphur is cooled rapidly (e.g. by pouring into cold water) plastic sulphur is formed, and this can be drawn out quickly into fibres. These are not stable, however, and rapidly revert to ordinary crystalline sulphur, but X-ray examination has shown that this plastic form consists of chains of sulphur atoms. The stable molecule of oxygen is O_2, though the atoms are not linked together by a simple electron-pair bond but by a double bond in which four electrons are involved. Sulphur also forms diatomic molecules at high temperatures, but at ordinary temperatures prefers to form two single bonds. The next member of this family, selenium, behaves like sulphur, having crystalline forms containing in one case Se_8 molecules and in the other, infinite chains of atoms extending throughout the crystal.

In Group 5 we find that the first member, nitrogen, resembles the first member of Group 6 in preferring a multiple bond in the elementary state, though it forms many simple molecules in which it is forming three electron-pair bonds:

$$\text{compare } N{\equiv}N \quad \text{with} \quad N{\lt}\begin{matrix}H\\H,\\H\end{matrix} \qquad N{\lt}\begin{matrix}F\\F,\\F\end{matrix} \quad \text{etc.}$$

The second element, phosphorus, behaves like sulphur in forming its 8-N bonds in the white and black forms of the element.

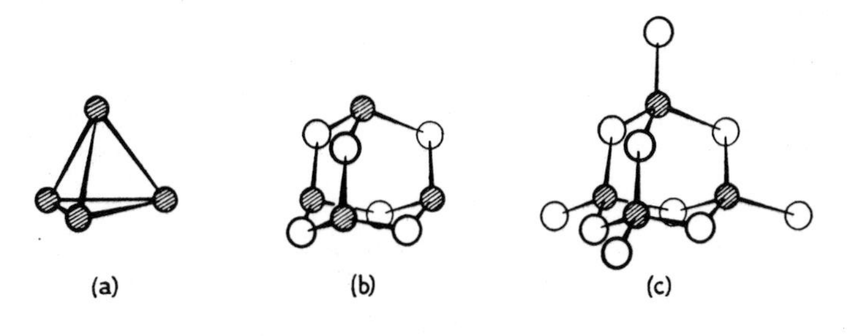

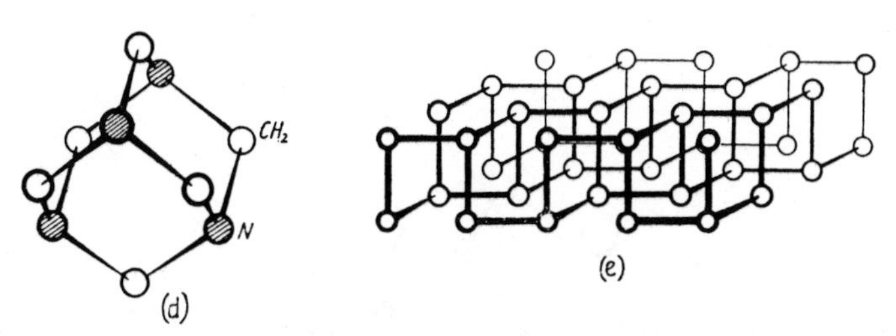

FIG. 89. The structures of the molecules (*a*) P_4, (*b*) P_4O_6, (*c*) P_4O_{10}, and (*d*) $N_4(CH_2)_6$. (*e*) Part of a layer in crystalline black phosphorus.

Instead of the simple ring and chain of sulphur (forming two bonds) we have now the possibility of arrangements extending indefinitely in two or three dimensions. In elementary phosphorus two of the simplest possibilities for an element forming three bonds are realized, namely, the tetrahedron and the plane hexagonal net (Fig. 89). In crystalline black phosphorus the atoms are arranged in double layers, and although it will not be immediately apparent that the arrangement is the hexagonal net it would be found that if the layer of Fig. 89 (*e*) is pulled out so that all the atoms lie in one plane, they are in fact joined up in the same way as the arsenic atoms in Fig. 90. (The reason for the buckling of the layer is that in the planar net the angles between the bonds would be 120°, whereas when phosphorus forms three bonds the inter-bond angles are close to 90° for

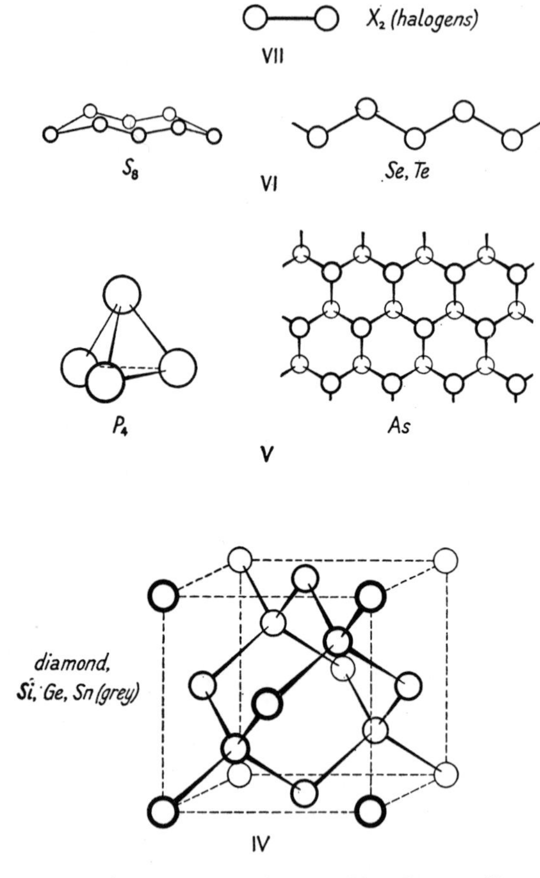

FIG. 90. Atomic arrangements in crystalline elements illustrating the formation of (8-N) bonds.

maximum stability. The further contraction of these angles to 60° in the tetrahedral molecule P_4 is apparently due to the fact that in this very compact grouping further interaction between the electrons of different atoms contributes to the stability of the molecule.) The atomic arrangement is more readily seen in the crystal structure of the ordinary 'metallic' form of arsenic. In this crystal the layers are much less distorted and the hexagonal net is easily recognized (Fig. 90).

In elements of the fourth Periodic Group there arises the possibility of very simple 3-dimensional framework structures in which each atom is linked to four others. The simplest 3-dimensional 4-connected framework has already been noted in Chapter III, and its most symmetrical configuration is the structure of diamond, silicon, and also of grey tin and germanium, two other elements of this group. These structures illustrating the formation of 8-N bonds are shown in Fig. 90.

The Highest Normal Oxides of Chlorine, Sulphur, Phosphorus, and Silicon

It is convenient to consider now the oxy-ions and highest normal oxides of these elements because the structural principles underlying the formation of complex oxy-ions are rather similar to those we have just been considering. We mentioned that these elements form tetrahedral ions SiO_4^{4-}, etc. An oxygen atom can form two bonds, and it is therefore possible for such groups to link up to form larger groupings. This process can go on until the neutral oxide is reached. In the case of chlorine only two ClO_4 groups have to be linked to form the neutral molecule Cl_2O_7

$$\begin{array}{c} O \\ O \\ O \end{array}\!\!\!\rightarrow Cl—O—Cl \leftarrow\!\!\!\begin{array}{c} O \\ O \\ O \end{array} \quad \text{or} \quad \begin{array}{c} \quad O \quad\;\; O \\ O : Cl \times O \times Cl : O \\ \quad O \quad\;\; O \end{array}$$

Chlorine, with seven valency electrons, can hold three singly attached (unshared) O atoms and one which is linked to a second Cl, in order to complete its octet of valency electrons. In the case of sulphur two of the O atoms of an SO_4 group can be shared with other similar groups so that we might expect closed rings or infinite chains of SO_4 groups joined up by sharing two O atoms with other groups. Sulphur trioxide is polymorphic. In one form there are infinite chain molecules, and in the other polymorph there are S_3O_9 molecules formed in this way

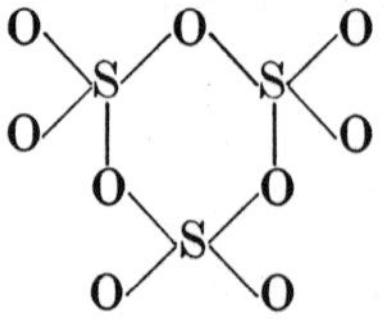

```
O      O      O
  \  /   \  /
   S       S
O/ |       | \O
   O       O
     \   /
       S
    O/   \O
```

from three SO_4 groups, each sharing two O atoms. It will be clear that if we focus attention on the tetrahedral MO_4 groups, which are being joined through their corners (representing O atoms), then the ways in which ClO_4, SO_4, PO_4, and SiO_4 groups can be joined up are exactly analogous to the ways in which Cl, S, P, or Si atoms are linked in the crystalline elements.

Element	*Oxide*	
Cl—	O_3Cl—O—	(Cl_2O_7)
 S<	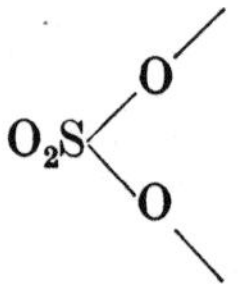 O_2S<(O—)(O—)	(SO_3)
 P< (3 bonds)	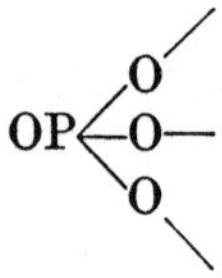 OP<(O—)(O—)(O—)	(P_2O_5)
 >Si<	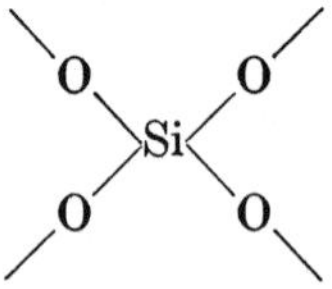 (—O)(—O)>Si<(O—)(O—)	(SiO_2)

Just as the structures of elementary phosphorus are to be found among the 3-connected nets so are those of crystalline phosphorus pentoxide, for in this oxide the structural units are PO_4 tetrahedra which are linked together by sharing three corners (O atoms) with other tetrahedra. Each P atom is thus joined to three others via oxygen atoms (*a*). There is, of course, a fourth oxygen atom attached to each phosphorus but since this is attached only to the one P atom it does not form an essential part of the phosphorus-oxygen framework. We can therefore simplify the structural scheme to that shown at (*b*), remembering that to 'regenerate' P_2O_5 we have to place an O

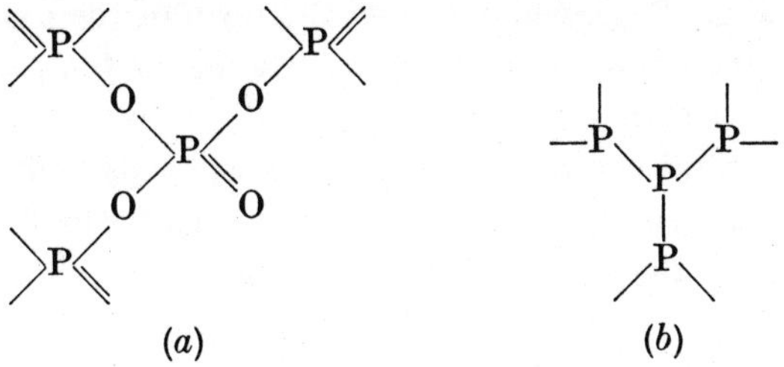

(*a*) (*b*)

atom along each link and a fourth oxygen attached to one P atom only (as at (*a*)).

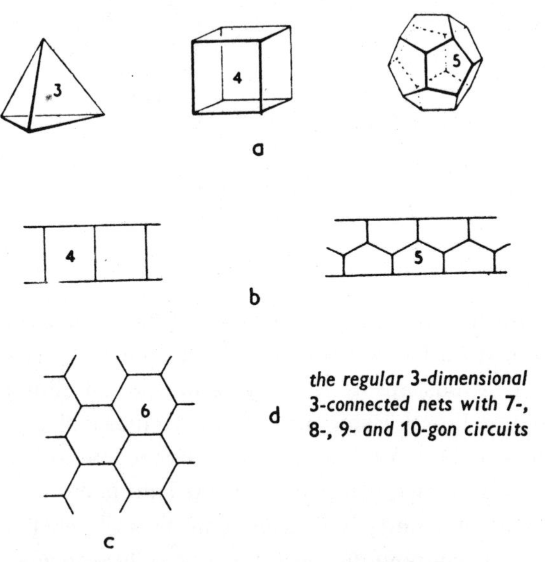

FIG. 91. The geometrical basis of the crystal chemistry of phosphorus and its oxides.

This oxide crystallizes in no fewer than three different forms (polymorphs), and two of these are very closely related, in this purely geometrical sense, to the structures of the forms of the element. We set out the simplest geometrical possibilities for P_2O_5 (or elementary phosphorus) in Fig. 91. First there are the finite systems, the most regular being those regular solids in which three edges meet at each vertex. One of the forms of the crystalline oxide consists of tetrahedral molecules of the type shown in Fig. 89 (*c*), which is also the form of the oxide in the vapour at moderate temperatures. (At higher temperatures it dissociates to P_2O_5 molecules.)

In the second crystalline form of phosphorus pentoxide the atoms are linked up to form layers, each of which is of the kind shown in the accompanying diagram:

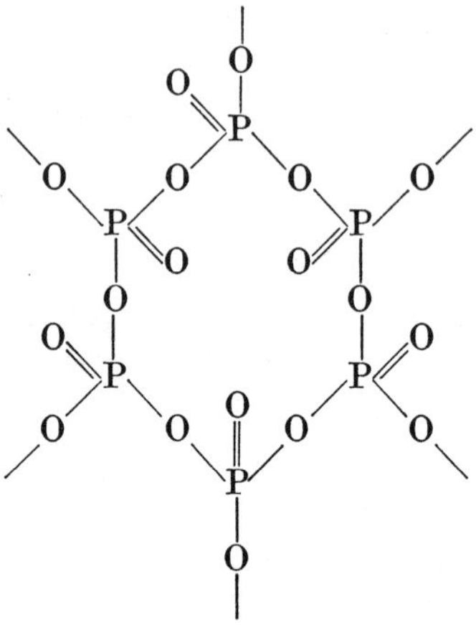

The phosphorus skeleton is the familiar hexagonal net. The third modification has a 3-dimensional framework structure in which the P atoms are at the points of the net illustrated in Fig. 37 (*b*) as a line drawing and shown stereoscopically in Fig. 92 (*b*), Plate XIII. We see that the structures of this oxide illustrate very beautifully the essential simplicity of the geometrical principles underlying the structural chemistry of certain groups of compounds. For the crystalline forms of P_2O_3 the structural scheme will be like that for P_2O_5 but without the fourth oxygen atom attached to each phosphorus. Nothing is yet known of the structure of crystalline phosphorus trioxide, but the situation is exactly similar for the trioxides and trisulphides of other members of the fifth Periodic Group such as arsenic and antimony.

The structures of these compounds do in fact provide further examples of the nets shown in Fig. 91. For instance, antimony trioxide has two crystalline modifications, one consisting of tetrahedral Sb_4O_6 molecules similar to those of P_4O_6 (Fig. 89 (*b*)), and the other is built of infinite chains

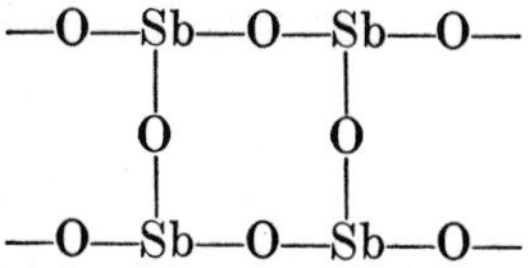

```
—O—Sb—O—Sb—O—
    |      |
    O      O
    |      |
—O—Sb—O—Sb—O—
```

Both As_2S_3 (the mineral orpiment) and one form of As_2O_3 have layer structures based on the same hexagonal net as already illustrated for one of the polymorphs of phosphorus pentoxide.

In the structures of P_2O_5 three of the four corners of the PO_4 tetrahedra are shared; this is the limit for these groups, giving the neutral oxide. If fewer than three corners are shared the result is a charged group of atoms (*complex ion*). The simplest example is the pyrophosphate ion, $P_2O_7^{4-}$. Very little is known of

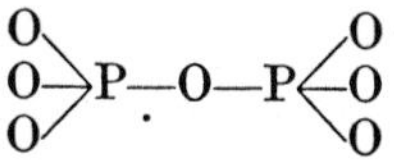

```
O\          /O
O—>P—O—P<—O
O/          \O
```

the structures of complex phosphates, of which the metaphosphates are a particularly interesting group. In these two corners of each PO_4 tetrahedron are shared with others so that rings and chains can be formed. A ring ion is found in aluminium metaphosphate, and although no example of an infinite chain ion has been found yet, this exists in the metavanadate $NaVO_3$. The following series of salts illustrates how the same type of formula can result from quite different atomic arrangements,

	Type of ion XO_3
$NaNO_3$	finite planar (*a*)
$Al(PO_3)_3$	finite cyclic ion (*b*)
$NaVO_3$	infinite chain ion (*c*)

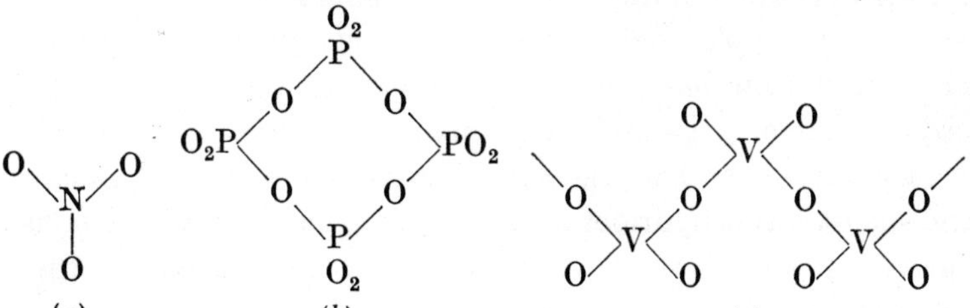

(*a*) (*b*) (*c*)

When we come to the silicates we shall find an even greater variety of groupings of SiO_4 tetrahedra. With these there are, of course, more possibilities since not only one, two, or three, but also four oxygen atoms of SiO_4 groups can be shared.

The Compounds of Carbon

These occupy a special position in chemistry because of their extraordinary variety and number (some half million are known) and because they are so intimately concerned with all forms of living organism, from the invisible bacteria and viruses to the largest animals, from the smallest form of plant life to the trees. Although the skeletons of some plants and animals are essentially mineral, particularly bone structures, the complex chemical processes involved in the growth of all living things are a matter of building up and breaking down compounds in which carbon is usually the major constituent.

There are two reasons for the great number and variety of carbon compounds; one is the fact that carbon can form either four (tetrahedral), three (coplanar), or two (collinear) bonds,

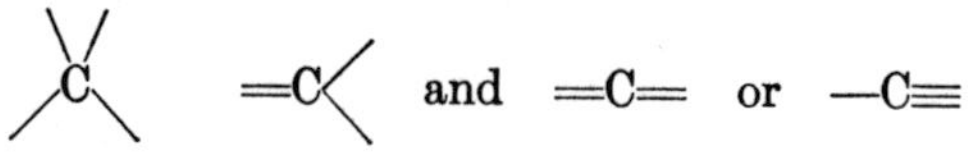

$$>C< \quad =C< \quad \text{and} \quad =C= \quad \text{or} \quad -C\equiv$$

though we should point out that this is not a property peculiar to carbon, and the other is the fact that a carbon atom forms bonds with great ease not only with atoms such as H, O, N, and S, but also with other carbon atoms. There is apparently no limit to the extent and complexity of the compounds so formed. Whereas compounds containing more than three nitrogen atoms linked together are unknown, or more than five or six sulphur atoms (plastic sulphur, with long chains, is unstable), there is no known limit to the number of carbon atoms which can be joined either in a simple chain or in a more complicated structure. The silicon atom has the same outer electronic structure as the carbon atom and resembles carbon in many ways. For example, elementary silicon has the same crystal structure as diamond, and silicon forms hydrides formally analogous to hydrocarbons, but very few of these compounds have been prepared and they are very unstable.

The simplest molecules in which carbon is forming four tetrahedral bonds are those of the type $Cabcd$, for example,

$$CH_4, \quad CF_4, \quad CHCl_3, \quad CH_2Cl_2, \quad \text{etc.}$$

At the beginning of Chapter V we indicated how numerous are even the hydrocarbons containing quite small numbers of linked carbon atoms; the number is greatly increased if we include compounds containing halogen as well as hydrogen atoms. A specially interesting molecule is that of 'adamantane', $C_{10}H_{16}$, which has the same general tetrahedral structure as P_4O_6 (Fig. 89 (*b*)) with CH replacing P and CH_2 in place of O. Geometrically it is simply a portion of the diamond structure, the remaining valencies of the outer atoms being satisfied by the addition of hydrogen atoms. Another molecule with the same tetrahedral structure is that of hexamethylene tetramine, $N_4(CH_2)_6$, in which N occupies the position of CH in adamantane (Fig. 89 (*d*)).

When carbon forms only three bonds, as in formaldehyde H.CHO, we may represent one as a double bond and the other two as single bonds:

O=C(H)(H) i.e. O::C:(H)(H)

In the carbonate ion, on the other hand, all three bonds are equivalent; they are of the same length and are symmetrically arranged at angles of 120° in a plane. This is the ion present in such familiar compounds as washing soda, $Na_2CO_3.10H_2O$, and limestone, $CaCO_3$. The simplest view to take of this ion would be to suppose that the carbon atom, initially possessing four electrons and having acquired two more in forming the CO_3^{2-} ion, has now six electrons with which it forms three electron-pair bonds and for which it supplies all the electrons.

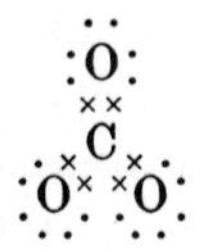

From the length of these bonds it appears, however, that some of the (unshared) electrons of the oxygen atoms are also used to some extent to strengthen the bonds.

In many molecules in which carbon is forming three bonds it is possible to write the formula in two ways, the single and double bonds being interchanged. An historically important example is the molecule of benzene

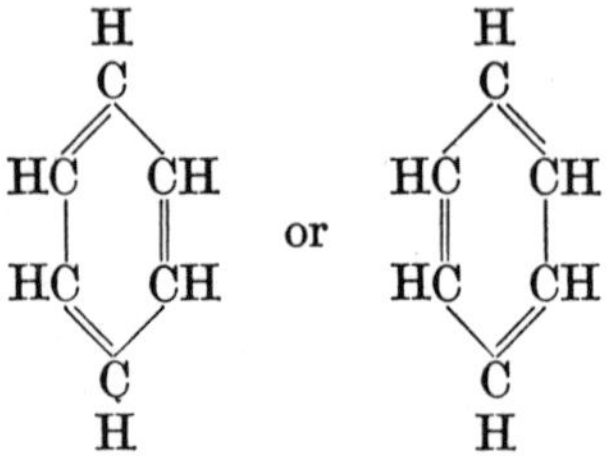

H H
C C
HC CH HC CH
or
HC CH HC CH
C C
H H

No difference is detectable between adjacent bonds and it appears that all the bonds are similar and in some way intermediate between single and double bonds. Molecules containing such rings of six carbon atoms form the basis of a very extensive chemistry. They are found in coal-tar, and also in some petroleums, from which they are separated by fractional distillation, and from the basic hydrocarbons

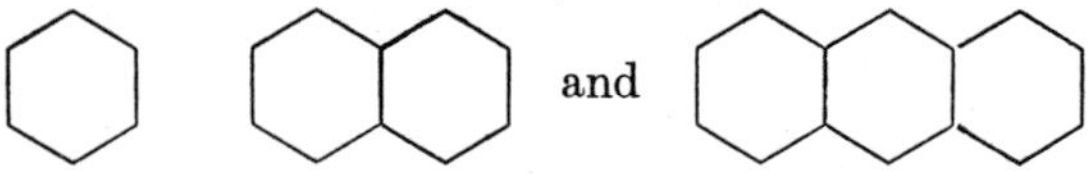

and

benzene naphthalene anthracene

and a small number of simple derivatives which also occur in coal-tar, notably

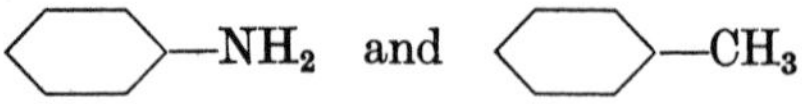

—NH_2 and —CH_3

aniline toluene

an extraordinary number of chemicals is produced, including dyes, drugs, disinfectants, explosives, synthetic resins, and fibres. Not only can the hydrogen atoms of any of the simple hydrocarbons be replaced by a variety of other atoms or groups of atoms, but in addition the simpler ring systems may be linked together to form much more complex molecules, as in the examples shown. Finally, it is possible to link certain groups of atoms together to form polymeric materials such as phenol-formaldehyde resins and the fibre-forming 'Terylene' which, like other synthetic polymers, is a valuable new textile material.

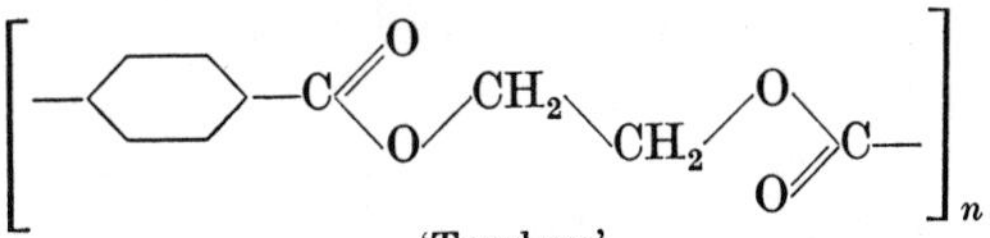

$$\left[-C_6H_4-C{\scriptstyle (=O)}-O-CH_2-CH_2-O-C{\scriptstyle (=O)}-\right]_n$$

'Terylene'

$$[-NH-(CH_2)_6-NH-CO-(CH_2)_4-CO-]_n$$

nylon

Compare with cellulose:

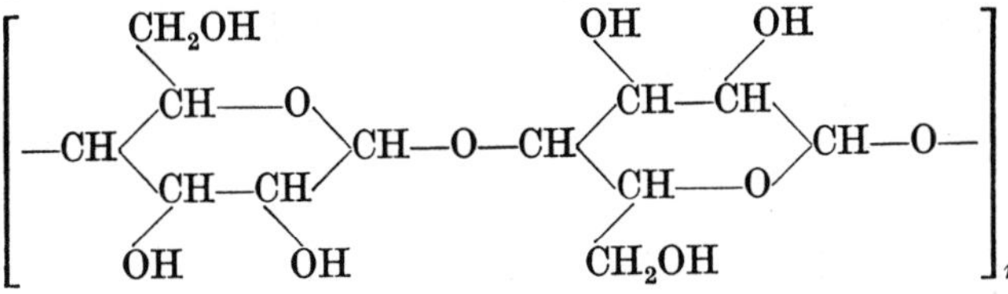

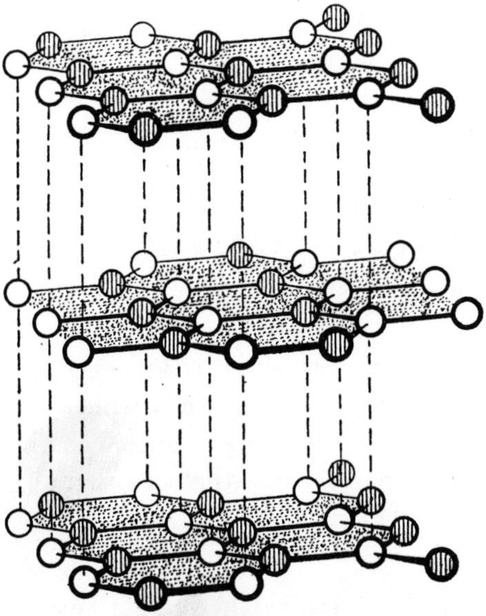

```
 [        CH2OH                       OH       OH            ]
          \                           \        /
          CH——O                       CH—CH
   —CH<        >CH—O—CH<                    >CH—O—
          CH—CH                       CH——O
          /     \                     /
         OH      OH                 CH2OH                    ]n
```

FIG. 93. The crystal structure of graphite.

The limit of fusing together rings of six carbon atoms is reached in the plane hexagonal sheets of the graphite structure (Fig. 93), in which there are only weak forces between the layers accounting for its properties as a lubricant.

Just as polyethylene (polythene) is the linear polymer

```
[ /CH2\     /CH2\     /CH2\ ]
[/     \CH2/     \CH2/     \]n
```

and is the end member of the 'paraffins', CH_4, CH_3CH_3, $CH_3.CH_2.CH_3$, etc., so graphite may be regarded as the end member of the fused-ring series starting with benzene, naphthalene, etc. We might have expected a 2-dimensional analogue of polythene with the formula $(CH)_n$ consisting of puckered rings, i.e. a hydrogenated graphite. Some of the simpler hydrogenated fused-ring compounds have been prepared, for example:

```
     CH2
    /   \                      CH2 CH2
 H2C     CH2                  /   \/   \
  |       |                H2C    CH   CH2
 H2C     CH2                |     |     |
    \   /                  H2C    CH   CH2
     CH2                      \   /\   /
                               CH2 CH2
```

```
                     CH2—CH2
       CH2—CH<               >CH—CH2
 H2C<          >CH—CH<                >CH2
       CH2—CH2               CH2—CH2
```

```
       CH2—CH2               CH2—CH2
 H2C<          >CH—CH<               >CH—CH2
       CH2—CH<        >CH—CH<               >CH2
              CH2—CH2               CH2—CH2
```

but on the whole not very much is known about the higher members of this family of compounds which appear to have little chemical interest or technical value. The final member of the series would be a layer like that of arsenic (Fig. 90) with CH instead of As.

Silicates

The outer surface of the earth consists largely of oxidized material. Although some of the most valuable minerals are not of this kind, for example, some metallic sulphides and the sources of power (coal and oil), these represent a very small part of the earth's crust, the greater part of which consists of silica either free or combined with oxides of other elements.

Silica itself, SiO_2, occurs in a variety of forms; as the colourless, predominant constituent of granites, as sandstone or quartzite rocks in which many metallic ores are found disseminated, as well-crystallized material (rock-crystal), in less pure forms as flint, chert, agate, and opal, and when broken down by weathering as the sand of deserts and sea-shores. Being an acidic oxide it combined with most of the more basic oxides of the metals to form silicates, which constitute most of the important rock-forming minerals and their breakdown products, the clays and soils.

As a result of the X-ray crystallographic studies which have been made of silicates we now know the atomic arrangement in many of them, and the structural chemistry of silicon rivals in interest that of carbon. Although not as extensive as that of carbon, the chemistry of silicon provides many beautiful examples of atomic architecture.

We have already illustrated the structure of diamond, in which every carbon atom is linked to four others arranged around it at the corners of a regular tetrahedron. This arrangement of atoms continues throughout the crystal, which can therefore be regarded as one giant molecule. Silicon also forms four tetrahedral bonds, and we have already noted that in elementary silicon there is the same arrangement of atoms as in diamond. The very important abrasive carborundum, silicon carbide SiC, which has a hardness close to that of diamond, adopts the same structure, alternate atoms being C and Si.

The basis of the structures of quartz and silicates is a tetrahedral group SiO_4 which can link up with similar groups by sharing one or more oxygen atoms. The isolated SiO_4 group is an ion carrying a charge of -4, and this occurs in combination with metal ions in such silicates as Ca_2SiO_4. Some compounds of this general type are formed in lime and sand mortars and plasters and in Portland cement. If only one oxygen atom is shared with another group the result is an ion $[O_3Si{-}O{-}SiO_3]^{6-}$ which is found in such silicates as the zinc ore hemimorphite, $Zn_4(OH)_2Si_2O_7$. This linking can proceed further, and if two oxygen atoms of each SiO_4 tetrahedron are shared we have the same geometrical possibilities as in the case of elementary sulphur, namely, the formation of closed rings or chains. Cyclic ions containing respectively three and six silicon atoms occur in the minerals benitoite, $BaTiSi_3O_9$, and beryl (emerald), $Be_3Al_2Si_6O_{18}$, and chain ions $(SiO_3)_n^{2n-}$ in enstatite, $MgSiO_3$, and diopside, $CaMg(SiO_3)_2$:

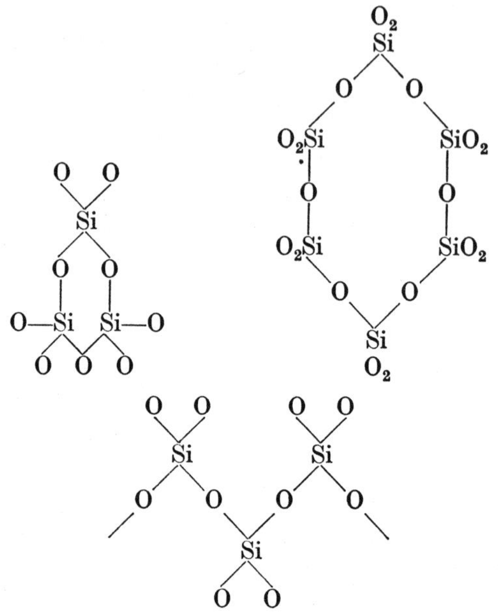

When three corners of each SiO_4 are shared with others a sheet structure is possible, extending indefinitely in two dimensions. Such sheets are a characteristic feature of the micas, a group of platy minerals some of which cleave into thin sheets which are valuable as thermal and electrical insulators, and the clay minerals. Talc (french chalk) owes its lubricating properties to its layer structure, the forces holding the layers together being relatively weak so that on shearing the crystal one layer slides over another. The silicon skeleton in most of these layers is the hexagonal net (Fig. 94 (*a*)) which we have met in so many other connexions, though another of the planar nets of Fig. 17 is represented by the structure of the mineral apophyllite (Fig. 94 (*b*)).

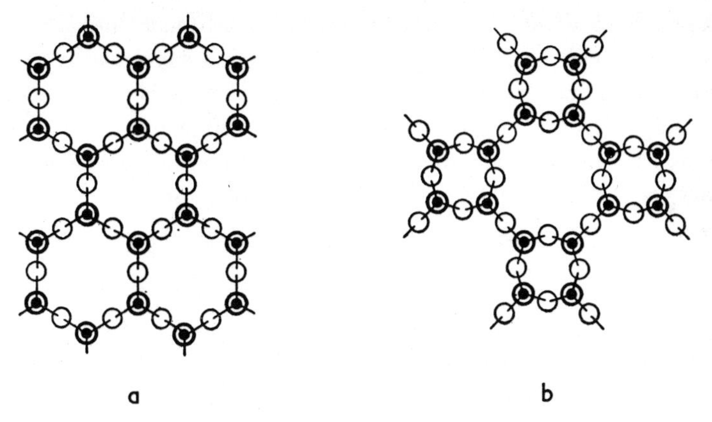

FIG. 94. Two layers formed by linking up SiO_4 tetrahedra through their corners. The small black circles represent Si atoms and the open circles oxygen atoms.

Three-dimensional framework structures become possible when all four corners of the SiO_4 group are shared, the situation being

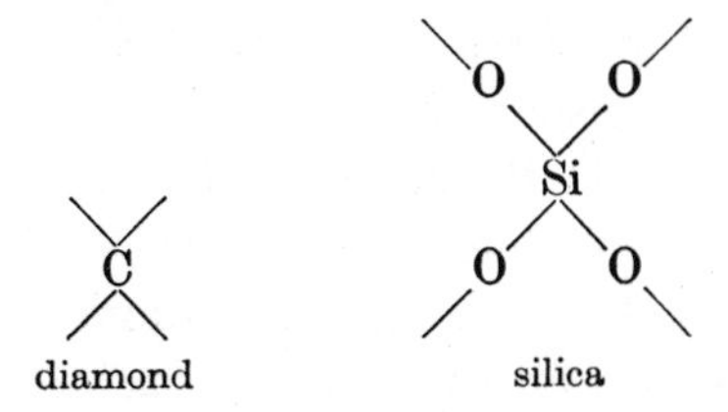

similar to that in the diamond structure. Silica, or silicon dioxide SiO_2, crystallizes with three different structures (Fig. 95, Plate XIV). In one form, the mineral cristobalite, the Si atoms are arranged in exactly the same way as the carbon atoms in diamond but are, of course, joined through oxygen atoms. We may think of these structures either as 4-connected networks in which the points represent Si atoms with oxygen atoms along each link or as assemblies of tetrahedra joined through their corners.

Frameworks in which all four oxygen atoms of each SiO_4 tetrahedron are shared with other Si atoms are electrically neutral and have the composition SiO_2. Some interesting structures arise if some of the silicon atoms are replaced by aluminium, for then the framework acquires a negative charge (minus 1 for each Al replacing Si) and is in effect a 3-dimensional ion. To restore electrical neutrality it is necessary to have positive ions such as Na^+ or Ca^{2+} in the interstices of the framework. A great variety of framework structures is now possible according to the proportion of silicon replaced by aluminium and the nature of the positive ions, as shown by the following formulae:

felspars	$K[AlSi_3O_8]$	zeolite	$Na[AlSi_2O_6]H_2O$
	$Ba[Al_2Si_2O_8]$	ultramarine	$Na_8[Al_6Si_6O_{24}]S$

It will be noticed that in all cases the number of oxygen atoms in the framework must be equal to twice the sum of the numbers of Si and Al atoms.

The felspars are the most important rock-forming minerals. The structure of paracelsian, $Ba[Al_2Si_2O_8]$, is selected to illustrate a felspar structure (Fig. 96 (*a*), Plate XV). Another group of framework silicates, the zeolites, contain water in the interstices of the structure, in addition to the positive ions. They exhibit the property described as 'base exchange' or 'ion exchange', that is, the positive ions which are situated along with the water molecules in the holes in the structure can be exchanged for other positive ions. This is the basis of the 'permutite' method of water-softening. The sodium-containing zeolite exchanges its Na^+ ions for Ca^{2+} ions taken from the hard water, the process being reversed when the zeolite is regenerated by treatment with brine. Fig. 96 (*b*), Plate XV, shows a zeolite framework, without interstitial material.

Ultramarine, which is responsible for the beautiful blue colour of the mineral lapis lazuli, and was at one time well known as the 'blue' used in laundering clothes, is one of a third family of silicate structures based on 3-dimensional frameworks. The framework is related to Fedorov's space-filling by truncated octahedra (Fig. 50 (*c*), Plate X), and is illustrated as a packing of tetrahedra in Fig. 96 (*c*), Plate XV. Within the framework are both positive and negative ions, the former being Na^+, Ca^{2+}, Ag^+, etc., and the latter Cl^-, S^{2-}, SO_4^{2-}, etc., and the colour depends on the nature of these ions, ranging from colourless through yellow and red to violets and blues.

Ice and Hydrogen Peroxide

We referred in Chapter V to the fact that the molecule of water behaves as if it possesses a tetrahedral distribution of charges, two positive and two negative. When water crystallizes the molecules therefore arrange themselves so that each is surrounded tetrahedrally by four others, and the molecules lie at the points of a 4-connected net. The arrangement adopted is not the simplest 4-connected net, the diamond net of Fig. 38 (*a*), but one very closely related to it. We illustrate in Fig. 95, Plate XIV, the structures of the three forms of silica as assemblies of tetrahedra (representing SiO_4 groups) and we pointed out that the cristobalite structure arises by placing Si atoms at the points of the diamond net and O atoms along the links. The centres of the tetrahedra are therefore the positions of the C atoms of the diamond structure. Comparison of Figs. 95 (*a*) and (*b*) shows that these structures are very closely related, the layers being the same in both but arranged differently relative to one another in the two cases. The positions of the centres of the tetrahedra in Fig. 95 (*b*) correspond to a 4-connected network rather similar to that of diamond and to the positions of the water molecules in ordinary ice.

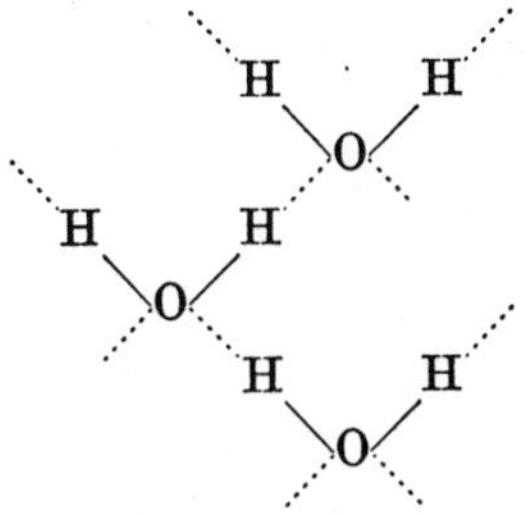

The water molecules are so oriented that each hydrogen atom points towards one of the negative regions of an adjacent water molecule, as in the accompanying sketch. It might be expected that H_2O molecules would form more open 4-connected networks such as those mentioned at the end of Chapter III. Such structures with large polyhedral holes are stable only if the holes are occupied, and it appears that if other atoms or molecules are present when water crystallizes then the water molecules do form open frameworks of this kind, linking up around the 'foreign' atoms or molecules which then become enclosed in polyhedral cages. Two structures of this kind which have been proposed as the structures of actual hydrates are illustrated in Fig. 50 (*a*) and (*b*), Plate X, as polyhedral packings in which four edges meet at each point, as required for any system of water molecules linked in the way we have indicated. There is no chemical bonding between the molecules in the holes and the water molecules of the framework, and such structures are formed even with atoms of inert gases (argon and krypton).

We should perhaps point out that these 'framework hydrates', being ice-like structures, are stable only at low temperatures. The structures of salt hydrates that we handle in the laboratory are quite different. In some of these (e.g. $BeSO_4.4H_2O$) all the water molecules are packed around the metal ions and the whole system of metal ions, water molecules, oxy-ions or other anions, forms a tightly packed arrangement which we can illustrate diagrammatically:

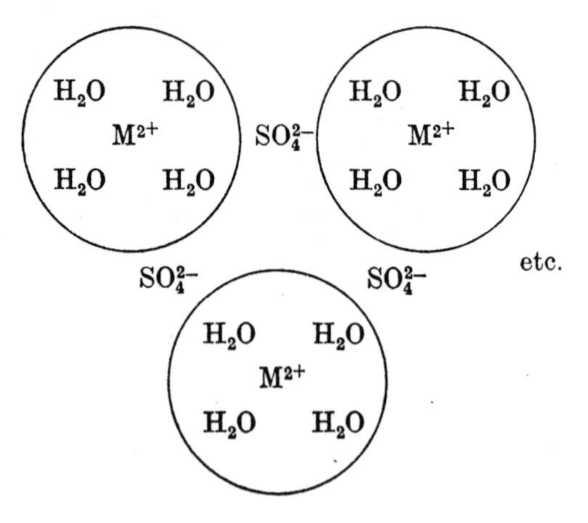

If there are more water molecules than can be packed around the metal ions, as in $NiSO_4.7H_2O$, they have to be accommodated between the oxy-ions and the $[M(H_2O)_n]$ groups; if there are fewer water molecules than the number required to complete the coordination group around the metal ion, the coordination group may be made up partly of water molecules and partly of oxygen atoms of oxy-ions:

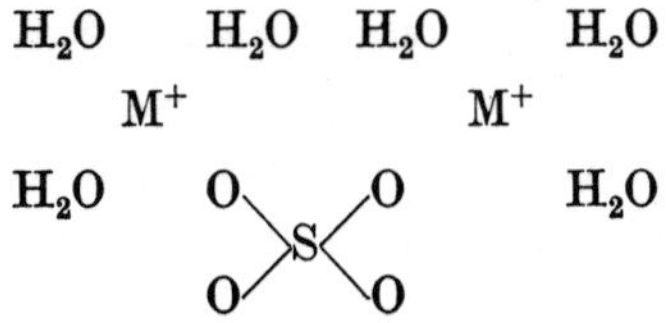

$$\begin{array}{cccccc} H_2O & & H_2O \quad H_2O & & H_2O \\ & M^+ & & M^+ & \\ H_2O & & O \diagdown \; \diagup O & & H_2O \\ & & \;\; S & & \\ & & O \diagup \; \diagdown O & & \end{array}$$

as in $LiSO_4.H_2O$. For another possibility see (*f*), p. 137. It will be evident that in general no simple relation is to be expected between the crystal structures of anhydrous salts and their hydrates, so that removal of water from the latter involves breakdown of the crystal and a radical rearrangement of the metal and oxy-ions to build the structure of the anhydrous salt.

Molecules containing hydroxyl groups also link up by means of hydrogen bridges O—H----O in crystals, and a molecule containing two OH groups (and therefore two H atoms) can, like H_2O, be linked to a total of four other molecules (as at (*a*)), or if we represent the O—H----O bridge as a broken line and

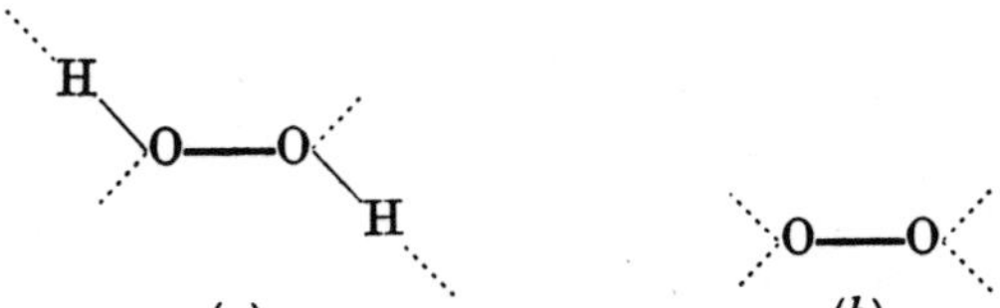

(*a*) (*b*)

the OH group as a circle we may simplify the structural unit as shown at (*b*). This could represent diagrammatically a molecule of the simplest possible dihydroxy compound, hydrogen peroxide, or equally a molecule such as hydroquinone (also called quinol):

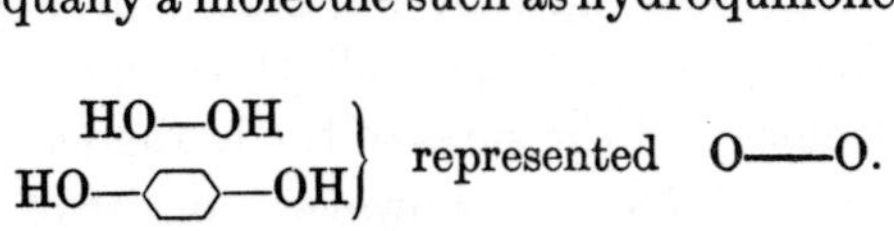

$$\left.\begin{array}{c} HO\text{—}OH \\ HO\text{—}\bigcirc\text{—}OH \end{array}\right\} \text{ represented } O\text{——}O.$$

It is now evident that the structures of crystalline dihydroxy compounds can be represented in this diagrammatic way as 3-connected nets (in which the points represent OH groups), and that we have the same general possibilities as described earlier in this chapter for any other structural unit that has to be joined to three others (e.g. PO_4 tetrahedra in P_2O_5). In fact it is found that in one form of crystalline hydroquinone the molecules are arranged in layers in which they are held together by hydrogen bridges in the way shown in Fig. 97. This is again our old friend the plane hexagonal net. For such molecules there is also the possibility of 3-dimensional networks of the kind described in Chapter III, and it is very satisfactory to find

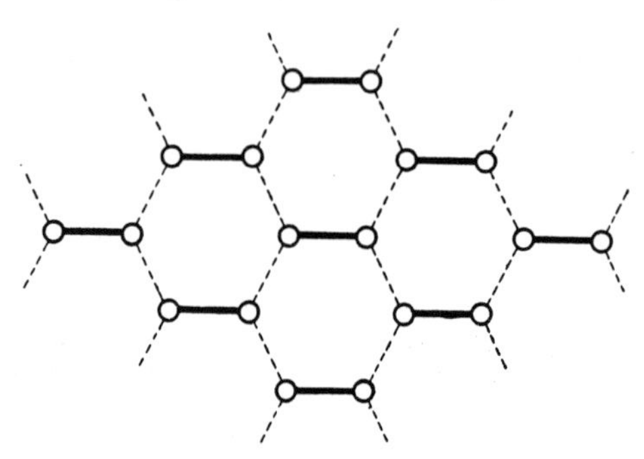

Fig. 97. Arrangement of molecules in one layer of a crystal of γ-hydroquinone (diagrammatic). Broken lines indicate O—H···O bonds.

that the idealized structure of crystalline hydrogen peroxide is one of the two simplest 3-dimensional 3-connected networks, that illustrated in Figs. 37 (*a*) (p. 47) and 92 (*a*), Plate XIII.

Just as water molecules form very open 4-connected framework structures by crystallizing around inert gas atoms or molecules such as SO_2 or $CHCl_3$ so hydroquinone forms an open 3-connected framework enclosing argon or sulphur dioxide when crystallized in the presence of these gases. In this case the framework in question is that illustrated in Figs. 37 (*c*) and 92 (*c*). The long slanting lines would then represent the hydroquinone molecules and the sides of the hexagons the O—H···O bonds. The crystal does not, however, consist of one such network, as in the inert gas hydrate structures, but of two identical interpenetrating frameworks.

Examination of the crystal structure of diamond shows that it is possible to travel from any atom to any other along C—C bonds, or in other words all the atoms of the structure form one connected system. This is generally true in crystals, but there is one notable exception among inorganic compounds. If oxygen atoms are placed at the points of the diamond network and a copper atom midway along each link, we have a network with the composition Cu_2O. Crystalline cuprous oxide consists of two interpenetrating frameworks of this kind (Fig. 98), one being simply translated relative to the other. Starting from an

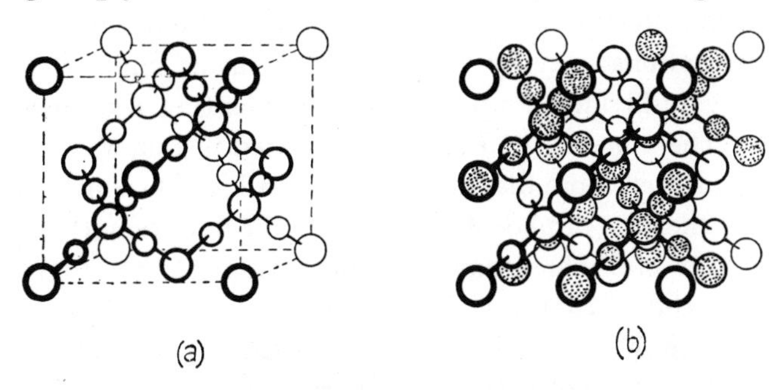

FIG. 98. The structure of crystalline Cu_2O (*b*) consisting of two independent interpenetrating frameworks of type (*a*). The shading is intended only to distinguish the two frameworks. The larger circles represent oxygen atoms.

atom which is shaded in Fig. 98(*b*) it is impossible to reach an unshaded one if we move along Cu—O bonds. In other words, there are no primary chemical bonds between atoms of the two frameworks. Many such structures consisting of sets of interpenetrating frameworks can be visualized, but the only other one so far found in a crystal is that representing the structure of the second crystalline form of hydroquinone. In Fig. 99, Plate XVI, the small hexagons represent the benzene rings of $HO.C_6H_4.OH$ molecules and the sides of the larger hexagons the O—H····O bonds between sets of six OH groups. Atoms of argon or small molecules such as sulphur dioxide are incorporated between the hexagons of different frameworks, and once incorporated cannot be released until the crystal is broken up by dissolution or vaporization.

The Chemical Formulae of Solids

The examples we have given of the principles underlying the structures of some selected groups of compounds will perhaps serve as an introduction to structural chemistry. They show how the study of atomic arrangement in crystals has enlarged the scope of stereochemistry, which is the study of the spatial arrangement of atoms, to include not only the configurations of finite groups of atoms but also of systems extending indefinitely in one, two, or three dimensions.

We have illustrated many molecules and crystal structures in the conventional way by drawing the atoms as small circles of arbitrary radii linked up by lines representing the chemical bonds. The molecule of P_4O_{10} is illustrated in this way in Fig. 89 (*c*) and even more diagrammatically in Fig. 91, which shows only the skeleton of phosphorus atoms. We have remarked that in many crystals the atoms, or a proportion of the atoms, for example, the relatively large oxygen atoms in crystalline silicates, are closely packed so that the structure may be regarded as a close-packing of spheres of a particular size. Although the representation of an atom as a rigid sphere of a certain size is also open to objection, it gives a much more realistic picture of a molecule or crystal structure than the 'ball-and-spoke' model, though for obvious reasons it is not suitable for illustrating crystal structures. It is well, therefore, to remember that atoms and molecules have shape and size, and for this reason we show in Fig. 100, Plate XVI, models of a number of molecules and complex ions. These models are not to scale and are intended to give only a general idea of the shapes of the molecules or ions. Only the larger O, N, or Cl atoms are included and H atoms are omitted.

The molecule of P_4O_{10} (Fig. 100 (*a*)), is now seen as a tetrahedral group of ten close-packed oxygen atoms. The complex ion in the cobaltammine with the rather forbidding formula

$$[Co\{(OH)_2Co(NH_3)_4\}_3]Br_6$$

is seen to consist of a central octahedral $Co(OH)_6$ group sharing three of its edges with octahedral $[(OH)_2Co(NH_3)_4]$ groups, the more lightly coloured balls in the centre of the model representing OH groups. At (*c*) we show the dimeric Al_2Cl_6 or Fe_2Cl_6 molecule consisting of two tetrahedral groups having an edge in common (see p. 137). The model (*d*) represents the $[Si_3O_9]^{6-}$ ion referred to on pp. 126 and 137; the trimeric S_3O_9 molecule (p. 116) has a rather similar form.

We have now a much deeper understanding of the significance of the chemical formulae of solids. For example, by showing how the atoms are grouped in sodium 'pyroantimonate', which exists only in the solid state, we now know that the structural formula of this salt is $Na[Sb(OH)_6]$ and not $Na_2H_2Sb_2O_7 . 5H_2O$. We have seen that the ratio of O:X in a salt AXO_3 does not necessarily mean that every X atom is attached to three oxygen atoms, this being true only if the ion XO_3 exists as a finite group in the crystal. We have already mentioned the series of compounds $NaNO_3$, $Al(PO_3)_3$, and $NaVO_3$, and this point may be emphasized again by quoting the series:

AXO_3	*Nature of ion* XO_3	*Number of O atoms attached to each* X
$CaCO_3$	finite CO_3^{2-}	3
$MgSiO_3$	chain $Si_3O_9^{6-}$	4
$CaTiO_3$	no complex ion	6

In the last structure the Ca^{2+} ions and the O^{2-} ions together form a close-packed assembly with the smaller Ti^{4+} ions in certain of the 'octahedral' holes between groups of six oxygen ions (p. 106).

It becomes clear that a particular type of formula can be realized in various ways. A halide in which the ratio of halogen to other atoms is 5:1 could be:

$$\text{molecules } AX_5,$$

$$(AX_4)^+X^-,$$

$$(AX_4)^+(AX_6)^-,$$

or

$$\begin{array}{c}—X—A—X—A—X—. \\ \quad X_4 \qquad X_4\end{array}$$

In the last case octahedral groups AX_6 are sharing two opposite corners to form an infinite linear grouping with the composition AX_5. In fact, phosphorus pentachloride exists as discrete molecules PCl_5 in the vapour state, but as an aggregate of octahedral $(PCl_6)^-$ and tetrahedral $(PCl_4)^+$ ions in the crystal. The complex halide Cs_3CoCl_5 is a crystalline aggregate of Cs^+, tetrahedral $(CoCl_4)^{2-}$, and discrete Cl^- ions.

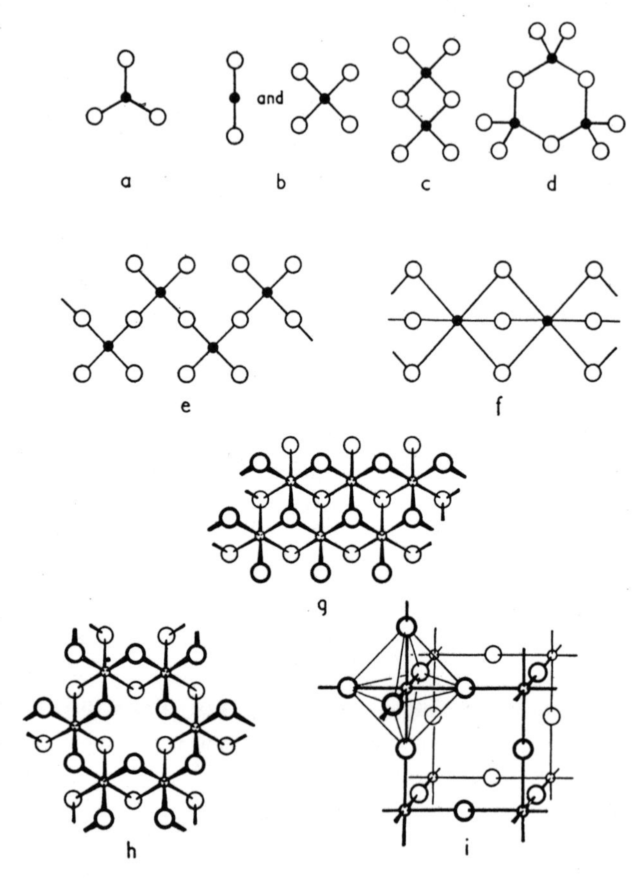

Fig. 101. Some ways of realizing a ratio of 3X : A in molecules or ions AX_3.

The number of ways of realizing a smaller ratio of X to A atoms is even greater, and some of the possibilities for AX_3 are illustrated in Fig. 101. It will be seen that they include a number of finite groupings as well as arrangements extending indefinitely in one, two, and three dimensions. Some readers may be interested in the following list of examples of the structures set out in Fig. 101.

(*a*) BO_3^{3-} and other oxy-ions.
(*b*) In the black crystals of $CsAuCl_3$ there are linear ions $(AuCl_2)^-$ containing monovalent gold and square planar ions $(AuCl_4)^-$ containing trivalent gold. The formula of this complex halide should preferably be written $Cs_2Au^IAu^{III}Cl_6$; there is a salt $Cs_2AgAuCl_6$ with the same structure.
(*c*) Fe_2Cl_6 and Al_2Cl_6 molecules.
(*d*) S_3O_9 molecule; $Si_3O_9^{6-}$ ion in $BaTiSi_3O_9$.
(*e*) $(CuCl_3)^-$ ion in $CsCuCl_3$; SiO_3^{2-} ion in $MgSiO_3$.
(*f*) The system of Li^+ ions and water molecules in $LiClO_4 \cdot 3H_2O$.
(*g*) $CdCl_3^-$ ion in NH_4CdCl_3 (p. 102).
(*h*) $CrCl_3$ layer (p. 102).
(*i*) ReO_3 structure (p. 100).

These examples could be multiplied, but what we have said should be sufficient to show why we have adopted a geometrical approach to structural chemistry.

It has been pointed out that in some structures there are holes large enough to accommodate foreign atoms or molecules. Not only can the composition of such compounds vary within certain limits according to the proportion of the holes occupied, but it can also be altered by exchanging one kind of foreign atom or ion for another. An even more unexpected result of the careful study of the compositions and structures of solids is the discovery that many very simple compounds can depart from the exact compositions corresponding to their chemical formulae. An example is ferrous sulphide, which occurs in Nature as the mineral pyrrhotite. The composition seldom, if ever, corresponds to the formula FeS, and formulae ranging from $Fe_{11}S_{12}$ to Fe_6S_7 have been assigned on the basis of chemical analysis. The arrangement of the sulphur atoms in FeS is such that the structure can tolerate the absence of a proportion of the Fe atoms, and in fact the non-stoichiometric materials are not sulphur-rich but iron-deficient. A pyrrhotite Fe_6S_7 is therefore preferably formulated $Fe_{0·86}S$. It will be appreciated that FeS is not an ideal compound to choose to illustrate the Law of Constant Composition.

In the Preface we mentioned that considerable regrouping of atoms takes place when some solids are dissolved or vaporized. In these last two chapters we have encountered many examples of such crystals containing infinite ions or molecules. We have concentrated on the structures of crystalline materials largely because crystals provide examples not only of finite but also infinite arrangements of atoms. It should be emphasized that we are not, in general, justified in drawing conclusions about the structure of a substance in other states of aggregation from the structure of the crystalline material. A single substance may have quite a structural chemistry of its own, as is well illustrated by ferric chloride.

In the vapour at low temperatures this compound exists in the form of Fe_2Cl_6 molecules (Fig. 100 (*c*), Plate XVI). When these condense to form a crystal a radical rearrangement of atoms takes place, and instead of a finite molecule in which every iron atom is attached to four chlorine atoms we have infinite 2-dimensional molecules in which every iron atom is surrounded by six chlorine atoms (p. 103). When this crystal dissolves in a solvent such as carbon disulphide the double molecules Fe_2Cl_6 re-form, but in ether simple tetrahedral molecules $(C_2H_5)_2O—FeCl_3$ are formed. We are accustomed to regard a process like the dissolution of a crystal as a simple reversible process, in the sense that removal of the solvent leads to the recovery of the original solute. This is generally true for non-polar solvents but not for dissolution in a highly polar solvent like water. When crystalline ferric chloride dissolves in water dissociation into Fe^{3+} and Cl^- ions takes place, and in the solution the former are closely surrounded by a group of water molecules which are strongly attracted to (and polarized by) the Fe^{3+} ion owing to its high charge and small size. Evaporation of the solution at ordinary temperatures leads to separation of a hydrate, and the original anhydrous ferric chloride cannot be recovered from the solution in this way.

We may summarize the structural chemistry of ferric chloride in the following way:

$[Fe(H_2O)_6]^{3+} + 3\,Cl^-$ ← Solution in water ← Anhydrous crystalline $FeCl_3$

$[Fe(H_2O)_6]^{3+} + 3\,Cl^-$ —evaporate→ $[Fe(H_2O)_6]Cl_3$ Crystals

Anhydrous crystalline $FeCl_3$ → Vapour or solution in non-polar solvent: $Cl_2Fe(Cl)_2FeCl_2$ —Higher temps.→ $FeCl_3$

Anhydrous crystalline $FeCl_3$ → Solution in ether: $Cl_3Fe \leftarrow O(C_2H_5)_2$

In this book we have not been concerned with the way in which the structures of crystals have been deduced. The reader who is interested in the methods used in determining the arrangements of atoms in crystals is referred to books dealing with the physical basis of X-ray crystallography. These methods are not applicable to vapours or solutions, and it should be remembered that a great amount of information about the structures of *finite* groups of atoms has been obtained by other methods. These range from those used by the organic chemist, involving degradation and synthesis, to spectroscopic and electron diffraction studies of gases and vapours.

INDEX

(*a*)

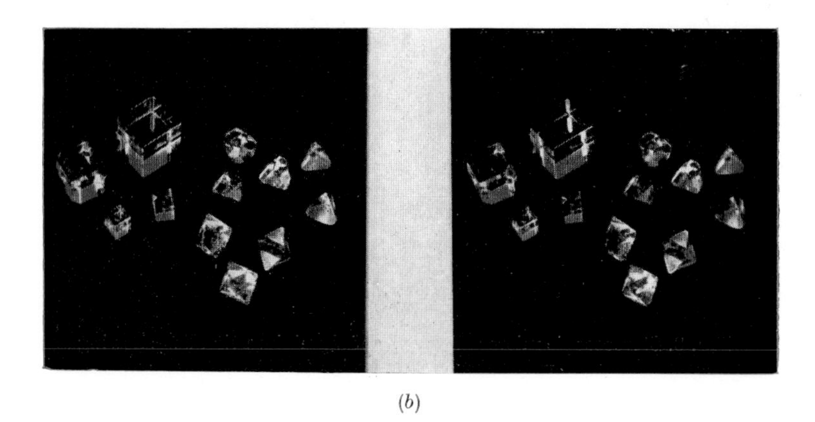

(*b*)

FIG. 5. (*a*) Natural crystals of quartz. (*b*) Crystals of sodium chlorate and alum grown in the laboratory. The three crystals in the foreground are those of alum.

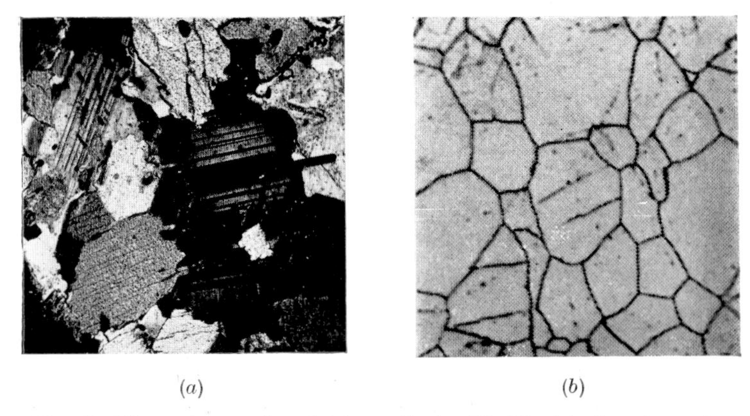

(*a*) (*b*)

FIG. 7. Photomicrographs of (*a*) granite ($\times 60$), (*b*) etched surface of a polycrystalline metal ($\times 50$), showing boundaries of crystals.

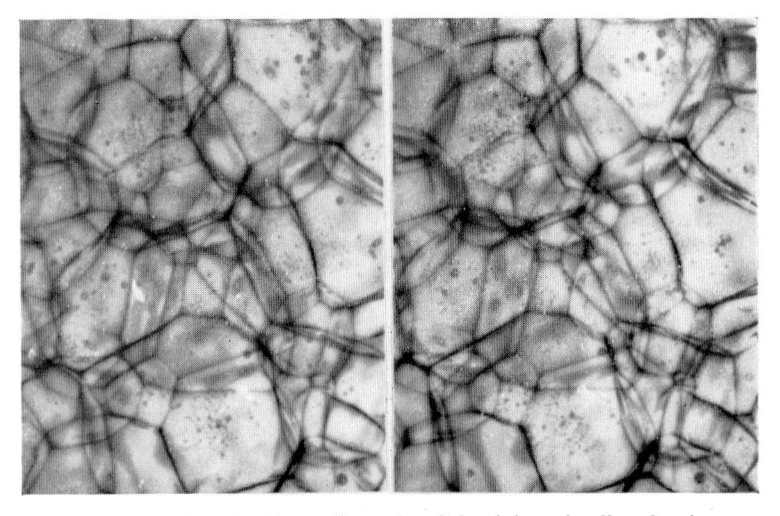

FIG. 8. Stereoscopic microradiographs of aluminium-tin alloy showing polyhedral crystal grains ($\times 35$).

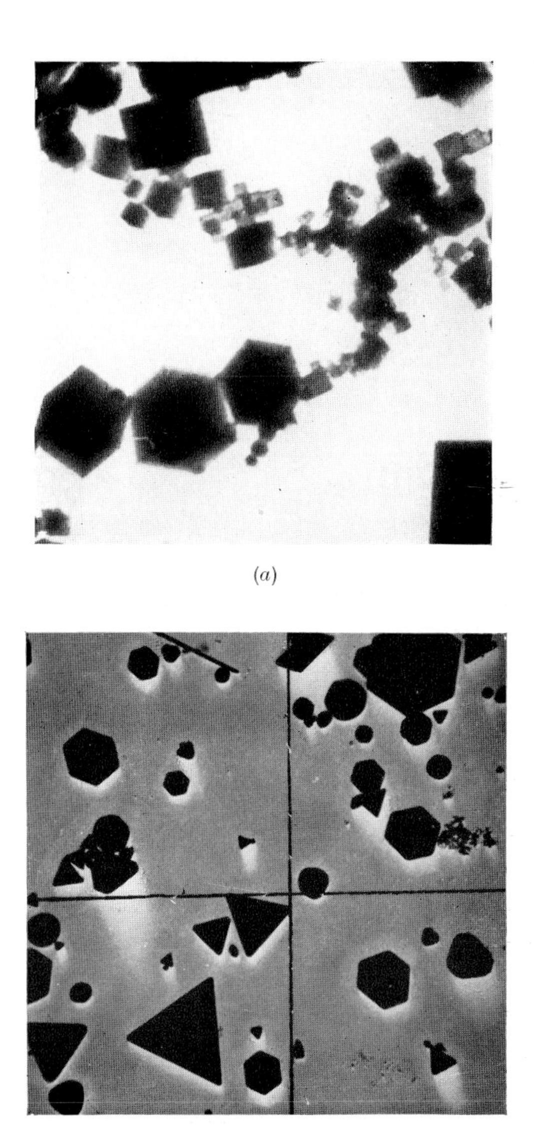

(a)

(b)

FIG. 9. Electron micrographs: (a) Magnesium oxide smoke. (b) Photographic film, showing silver halide crystals. The magnification is $\times 35{,}000$ for (a) and $\times 10{,}000$ for (b).

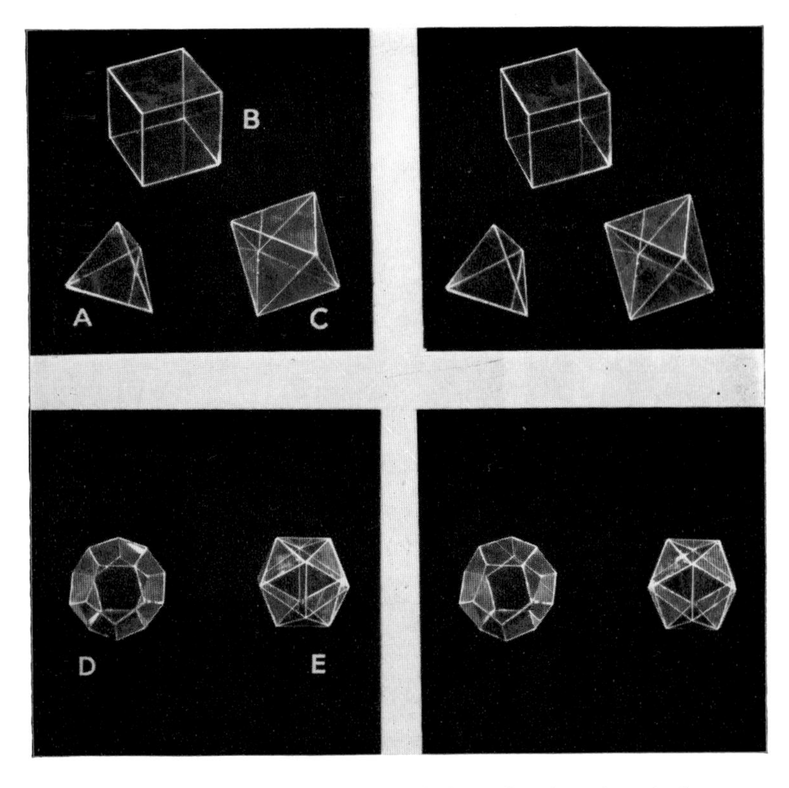

FIG. 25. The regular solids: (*a*) tetrahedron, (*b*) cube, (*c*) octahedron, (*d*) dodecahedron, (*e*) icosahedron.

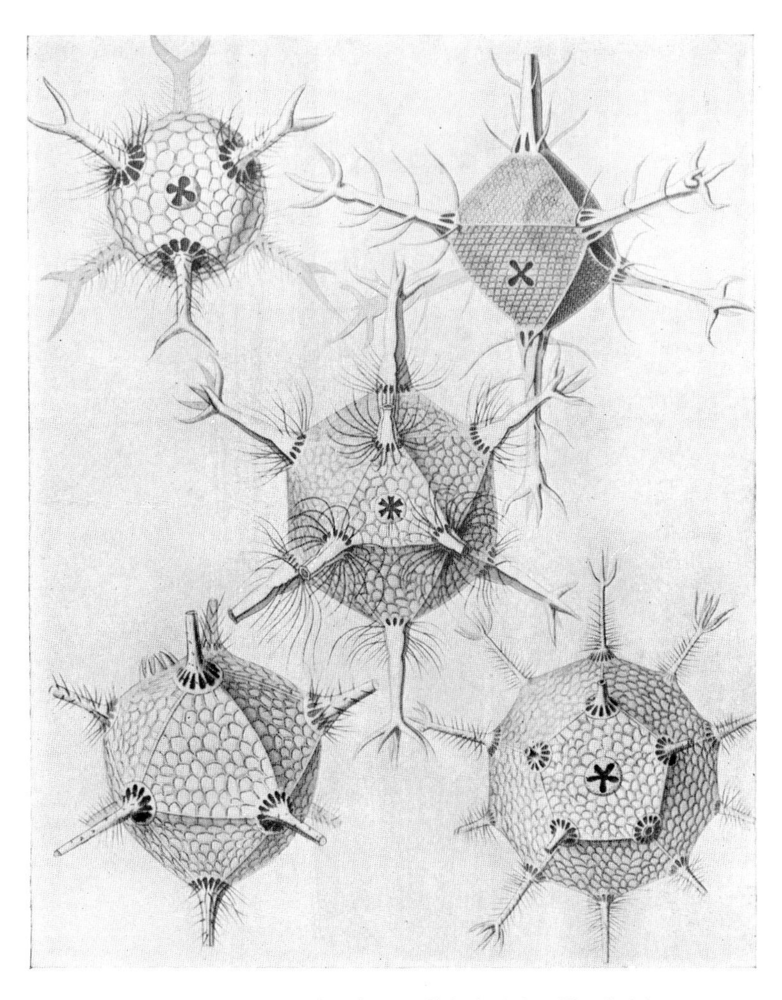

FIG. 26. Skeletons of various radiolaria (after Haeckel)*.

* There is considerable doubt as to whether certain of these skeletons (particularly the dodecahedral and icosahedral ones) ever existed, according to a statement by Sir D'Arcy Thompson quoted by H. S. M. Coxeter (*American Mathematical Monthly*, 1953, **60**, 137)

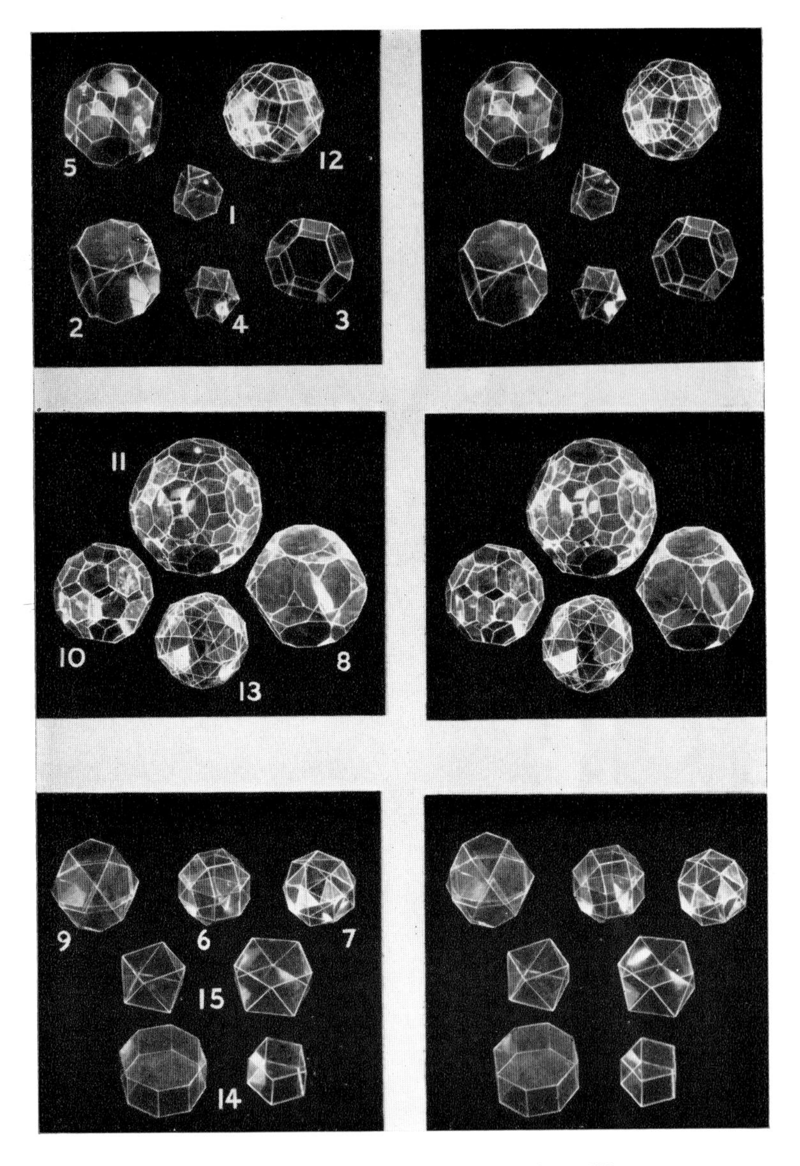

FIG. 28. The Archimedean semi-regular solids.

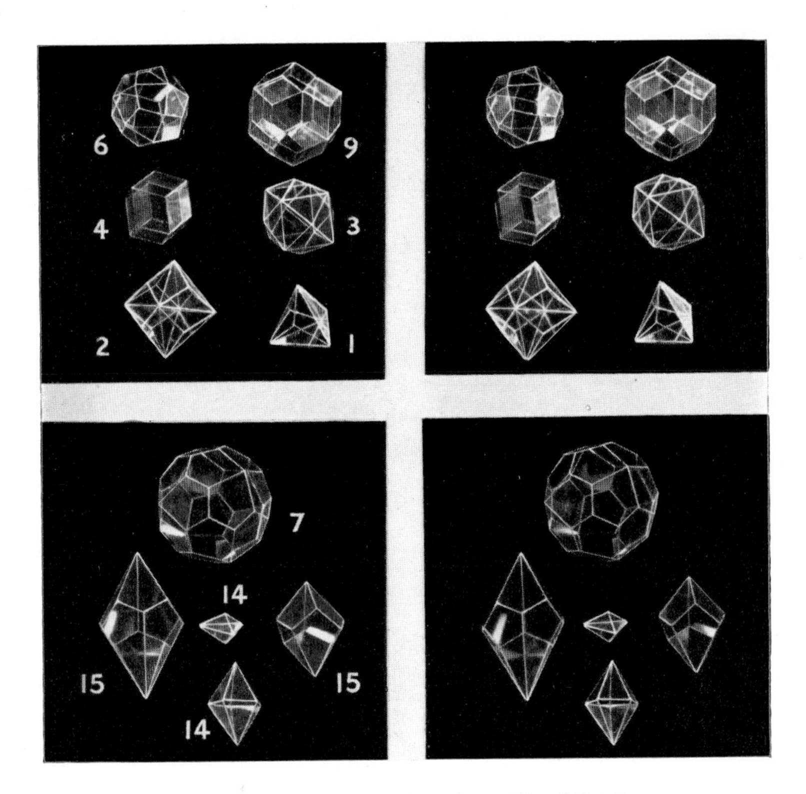

FIG. 30. Some of the semi-regular solids of Catalan.

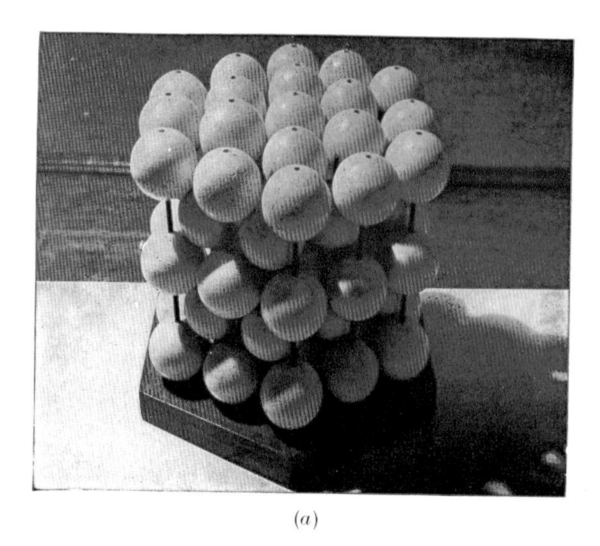

(*a*)

(*b*)

FIG. 43. The closest packing of equal spheres: (*a*) hexagonal closest packing, (*b*) cubic closest packing with atoms removed from one corner to show the close-packed layer

FIG. 45. Model of bees' honeycomb.

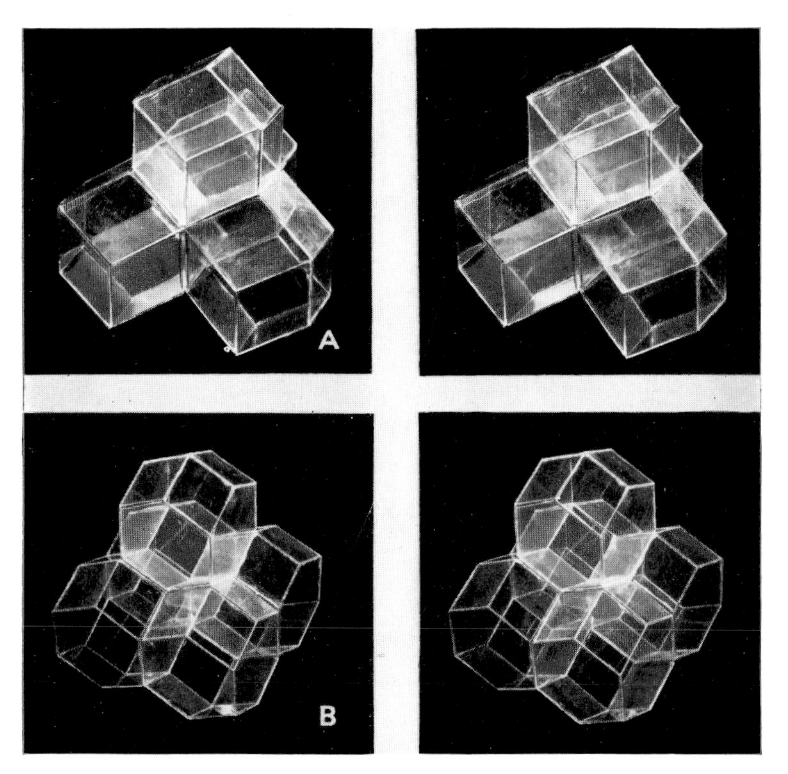

FIG. 49. Space-filling by (*a*) rhombic dodecahedra, (*b*) elongated dodecahedra.

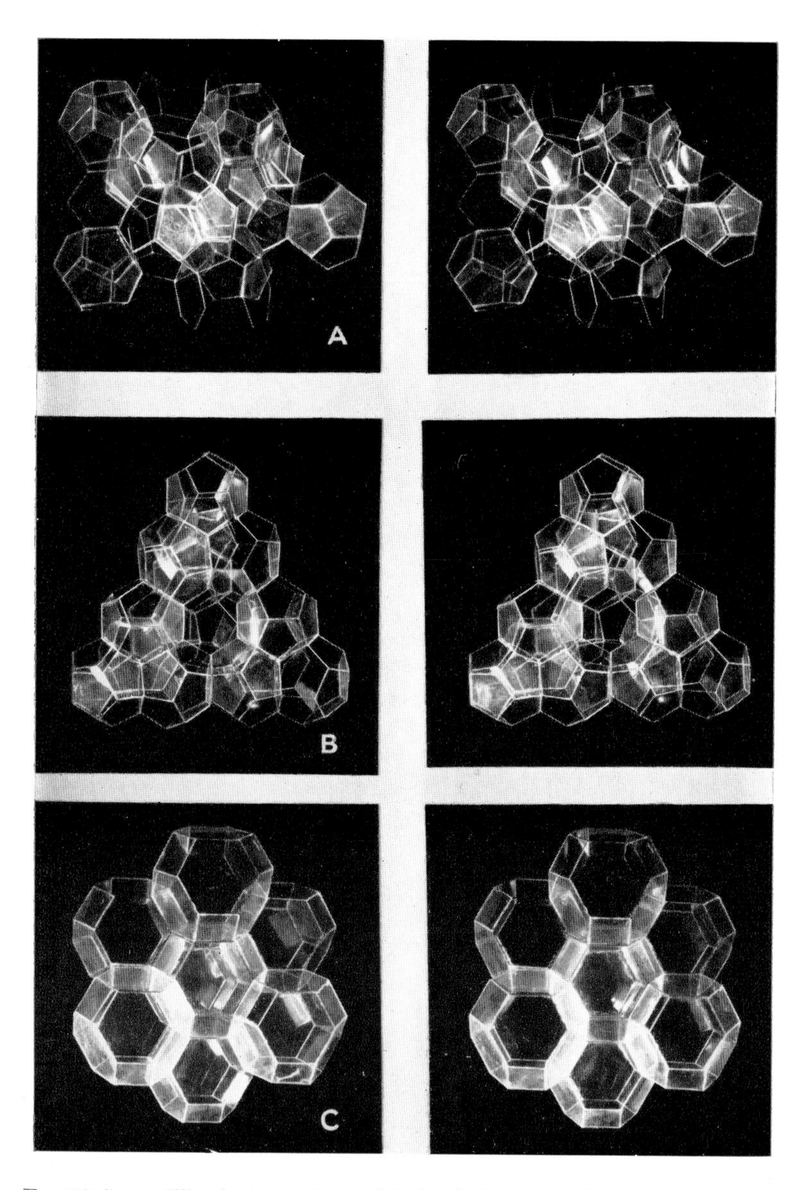

FIG. 50. Space-filling by (*a*) pentagonal dodecahedra and 14-hedra, (*b*) pentagonal dodecahedra and 16-hedra, and (*c*) truncated octahedra.

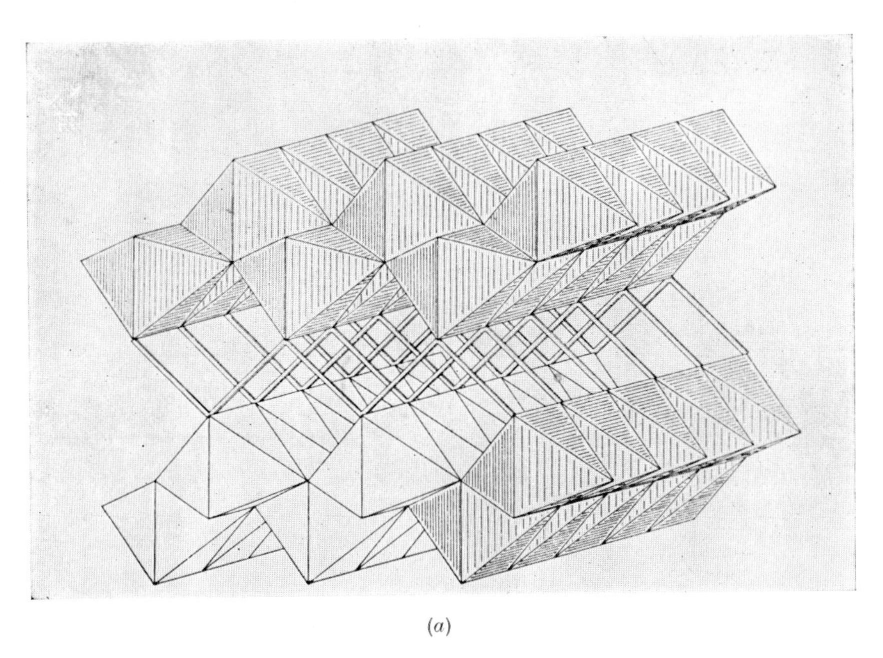

(*a*)

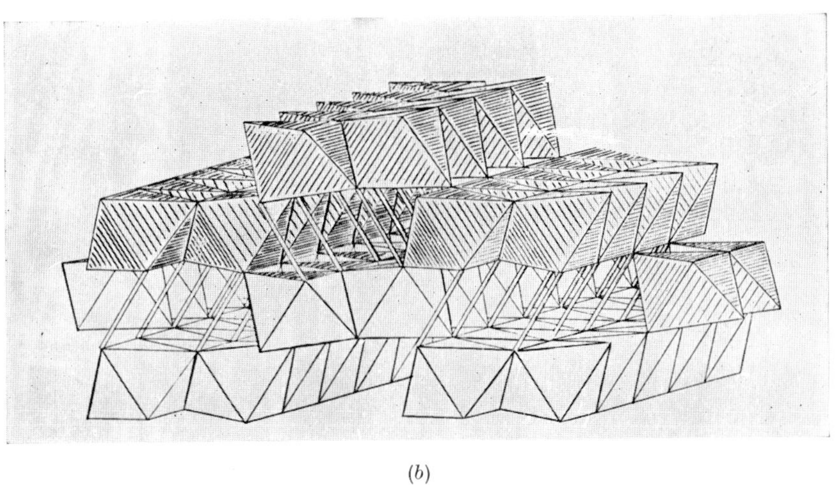

(*b*)

FIG. 86. Two structures built from double strings of octahedra, those of the two crystalline forms of AlO.OH (after Ewing).

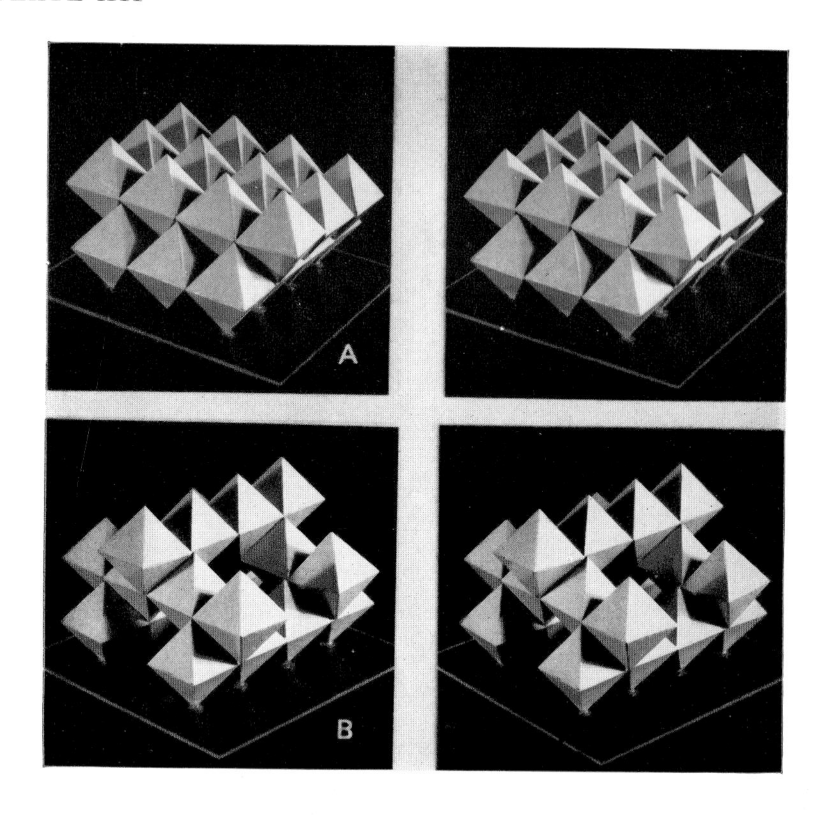

(*c*)

FIG. 88. The structures of (*a*) NaCl and (*b*) $Cu_2(OH)_3Cl$ represented as packings of octahedral coordination groups. (*c*) Layer of BiI_3 or $CrCl_3$ structures.

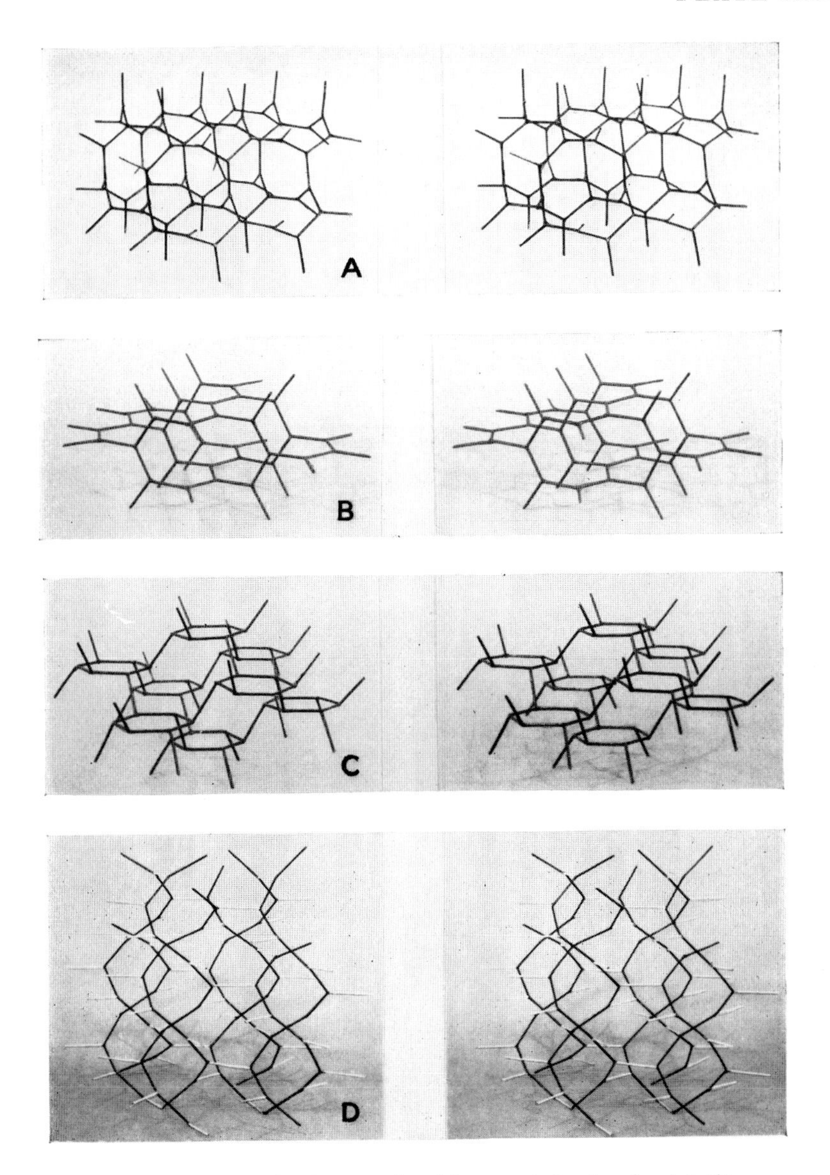

FIG. 92. Stereoscopic photographs of 3-connected networks: (*a*), (*b*), and (*c*), the nets of Fig. 37, (*d*) the net $12^2.14$ (see p. 49).

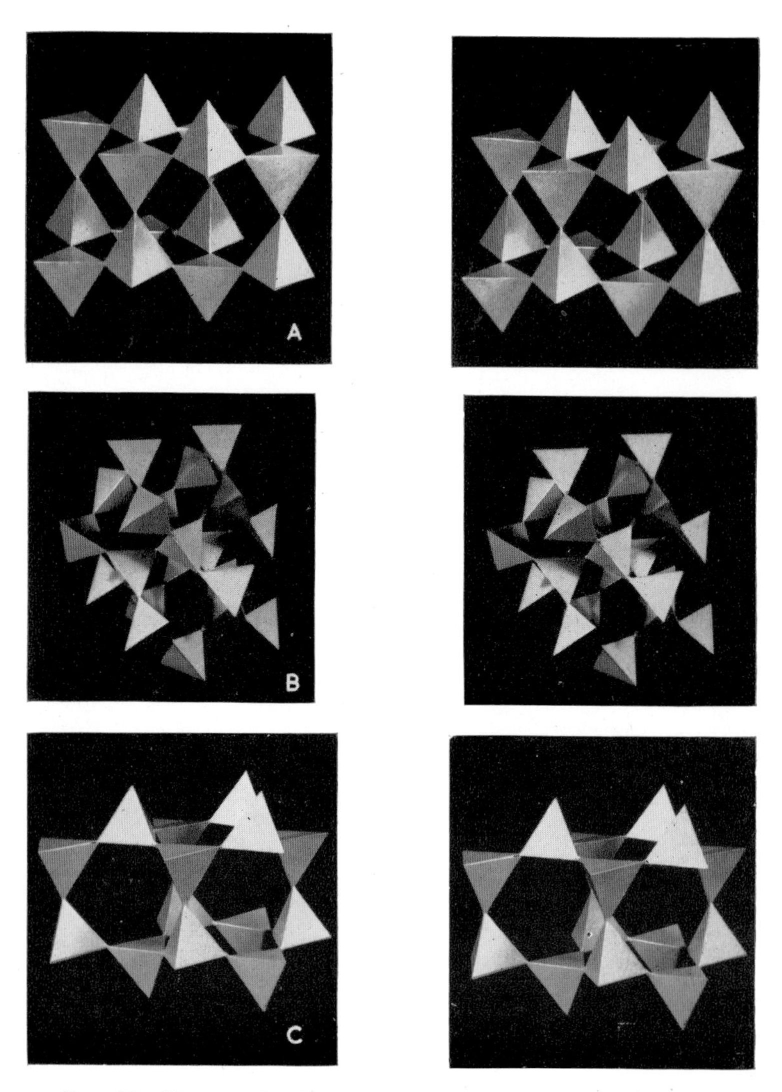

FIG. 95. Stereoscopic photographs showing the structures of the three forms of silica, (*a*) cristobalite, (*b*) quartz, and (*c*) tridymite, as systems of linked tetrahedra representing SiO_4 groups.

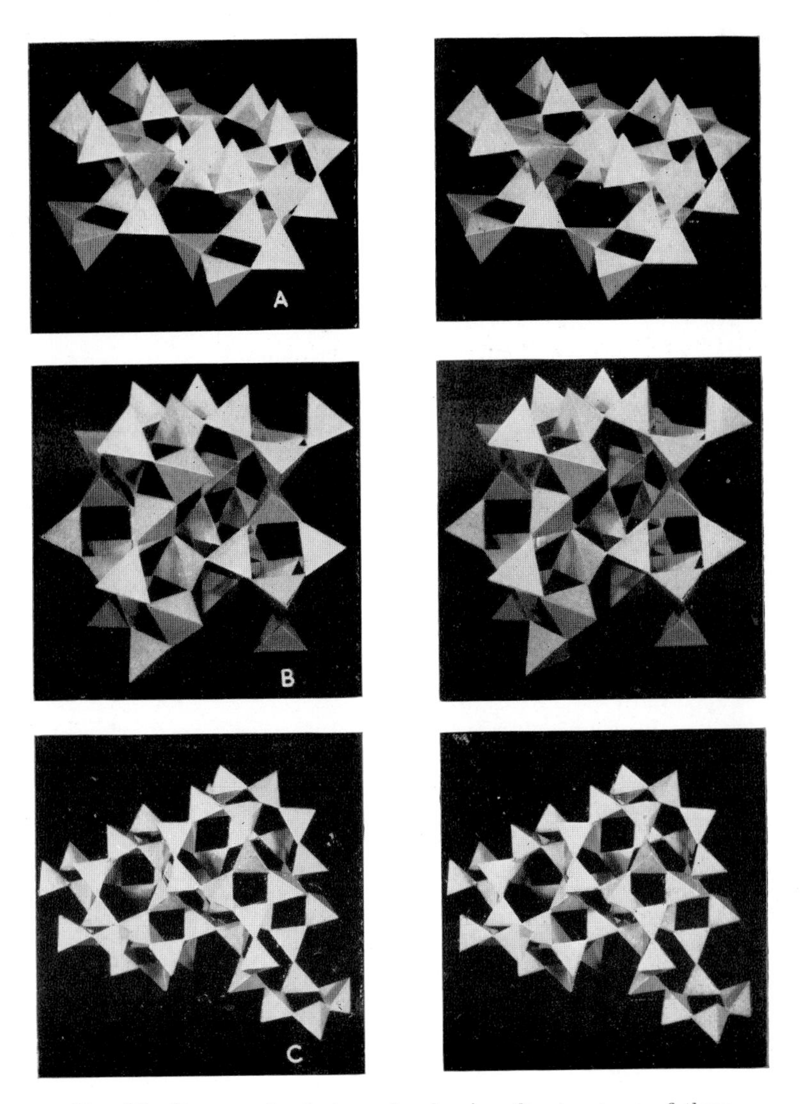

FIG. 96. Stereoscopic photographs showing the structures of three silicate minerals as frameworks of linked $(Si_1Al)O_4$ tetrahedra: (*a*) paracelsian, $Ba[Al_2Si_2O_8]$, (*b*) a zeolite, $Na[AlSi_2O_6].H_2O$, and (*c*) ultramarine, $Na_8[Al_6Si_6O_{24}]S$.

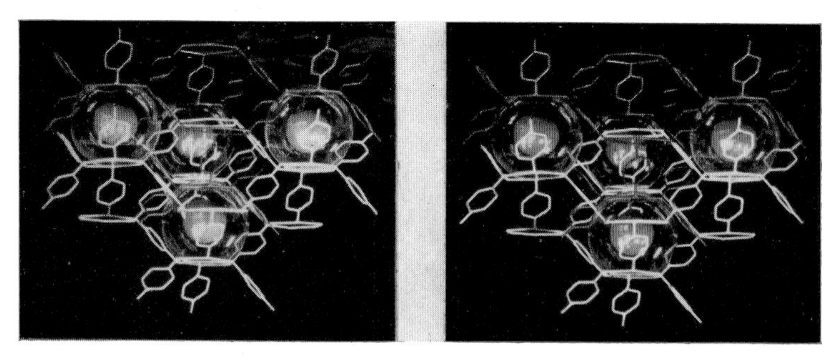

FIG. 99. The crystal structure of β-quinol, consisting of two interpenetrating frameworks. The balls inside the transparent spheres represent atoms of argon trapped in the interstices between the two frameworks.

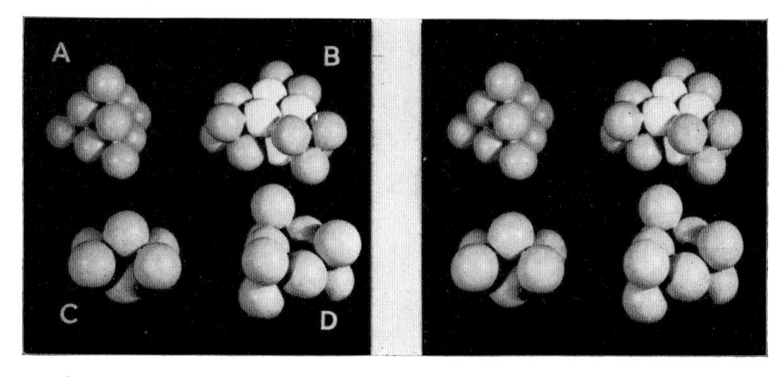

FIG. 100. Models representing some molecules and complex ions. (*a*) P_4O_{10}, (*b*) $[Co\{(OH)_2Co(NH_3)_4\}_3]^{6+}$, (*c*) Al_2Cl_6 or Fe_2Cl_6, (*d*) $[Si_3O_9]^{6-}$. Only the larger O, N, or Cl atoms are shown and H atoms are omitted.